# THE SIXTH WORLD FOOD SURVEY

## CENTRE FOR HUMAN NUTRITION
## LONDON SCHOOL OF HYGIENE
## AND TROPICAL MEDICINE

# The Sixth
# WORLD FOOD
# SURVEY

## 1 9 9 6

CENTRE FOR HUMAN NUTRITION
LONDON SCHOOL OF HYGIENE
AND TROPICAL MEDICINE

FOOD AND AGRICULTURE ORGANIZATION OF THE UNITED NATIONS
Rome, 1996

The designations employed and the presentation of material in this publication do not imply the expression of any opinion whatsoever on the part of the Food and Agriculture Organization of the United Nations concerning the legal status of any country, territory, city or area or of its authorities, or concerning the delimitation of its frontiers or boundaries.

P-87
ISBN 92-5-103837-6

# Foreword

It is very appropriate that *The Sixth World Food Survey* should be completed just before the World Food Summit that I have taken the initiative to convene in November 1996. The World Food Summit, which will bring together the heads of state and government from all regions of the world in Rome, will address a major problem facing today's world: hunger and food insecurity. The basic aim of FAO's world food surveys is to provide the information available on the levels and trends of world food supplies and the prevalence of food inadequacy and undernutrition. Thus, *The Sixth World Food Survey* will be a major contributor to the background information for deliberations on this subject at the Summit.

While the scope and contents of *The Sixth World Food Survey* are broadly similar to its predecessors, certain new features have been included. First, China and the former Asian centrally planned economies, which were previously excluded from traditional estimates of the prevalence of food inadequacy or undernutrition, are now included. Second, the methodology of estimation, while essentially the same as that of *The Fifth World Food Survey*, has been refined and improved in the light of improved knowledge. Third, there is now an expanded coverage of anthropometric indicators providing information on the nutritional status of subgroups such as children, adolescents and adults. Admittedly, however, the available data are still inadequate or imprecise for many countries and must therefore be supplemented by assumptions or the use of models in order to estimate the prevalence of food inadequacy. The solution to this problem depends crucially on the improvement of primary data collection efforts by countries. Therefore, I take this opportunity to urge member countries to assign a high priority to the collection and provision of basic data (production, trade, consumption and access to food by different population groups).

The main conclusion of the survey is that per caput dietary energy supplies have continued to increase in the developing countries as a whole, with the result that, during the two decades from 1969-71, the prevalence of food inadequacy declined: 20 percent of the total population had inadequate access to food in 1990-92 compared with 35 percent two decades ago. Even more remarkable was the improvement in absolute terms, i.e. fewer people faced inadequate food access in 1990-92 compared with 20 years ago, notwithstanding the addition of 1.5 billion people to the population of developing countries during this period. The number of people with inadequate access to food declined from 918 million in 1969-71 to 906 million in 1979-81 and further to 841 million in

v

1990-92. Nevertheless, this number was still very high in 1990-92, as one out of five people in the developing world faced food inadequacy.

*The Sixth World Food Survey* provides a wealth of data, especially in its Appendix tables which will hopefully assist national governments and international agencies in their joint effort to eliminate food inadequacy and undernutrition so that, one day in the not too distant future, food security may be guaranteed to all men and women everywhere.

**Jacques Diouf**
DIRECTOR-GENERAL

# Contents

viii

# Tables

ix

# Figures

xiii

# Boxes

## Acknowledgements

The Sixth World Food Survey *was prepared jointly by staff in the Statistics Division and the Food and Nutrition Division of the Economic and Social Department. The Statistics Division team was led by L. Naiken and included P. Lewchalermwongs and J. Mernies, with computational support provided by C. Cerri, F. de Vizioli-Meo, N. Martone and M. Barre and secretarial support by P. Blake. The Food and Nutrition Division team was led by J.-P. Cotier and included S. Chevassus-Agnes. Comments and reviews were provided by senior staff in other divisions of the department before finalizing this publication.*

*Contributions were also made by a number of consultants and external reviewers. D. Casley, J. Mason, W.P.T. James, M. Franklin and P. Naidu advised on the improvements in the methodology for estimating the prevalence of food inadequacy during informal expert group meetings; P. Rao prepared the draft of Appendix 3, Methodology for assessing food inadequacy in developing countries, on the basis of existing staff background papers; P. Payne provided advice and comments on the drafts of Chapter 2 and Appendix 3; P.S. Shetty prepared the original drafts of Chapter 3, Assessment of child and adult undernutrition in the developing countries, and Appendix 4, Anthropometric assessment of nutritional status. Chapter 3 also benefited from reviews and comments by J.C. Waterlow, W.P.T. James and A. Ferro-Luzzi; M.D.C. Immink assisted in the revision of Chapter 3 to incorporate the comments of the reviewers and provided useful inputs to the other chapters. Finally, S.R. Osmani technically edited and organized the various draft inputs into a consolidated document.*

The Sixth World Food Survey, *was edited by R. Tucker with B. McCarthy. The graphics were prepared by M. Cappucci and G. Maxwell, the layout by M. Criscuolo with F. Dicarlo.*

# Explanatory note

## Countries and country groups

The global analyses presented in this report are based on the data for countries which had a population of more than one million in 1990.

The 15 republics of the former USSR and the five republics of the former Yugoslavia have become independent states since 1991. However, since historical food balance sheets for these newly independent countries are not available, the analyses have had to be based on the data from the former USSR and the former Yugoslavia.

For analytical purposes, countries and territories are classified as developed or developing as well as by economic group. Developed countries comprise the industrialized countries and economies in transition. Developing countries are classified as low-income, middle-income or high-income countries. This income-based classification is used by the World Bank to determine eligibility for assistance from the International Development Association. Developing countries are also classified as least developed countries and low-income food-deficit countries. The composition of all country groups, including the regional groups, are shown in Appendix 1. The developing countries and economic groups are defined as follows:

*Developing countries.* According to the *Encyclopaedia Britannica*, there is no universally accepted definition of what a developing country is. Despite the wide differences among developing countries, they share a number of characteristics. In most developing countries, primary (agricultural or extractive) production accounts for a very large proportion of national income and, not infrequently, a disproportionate share is taken up by one or two products. The level and range of secondary industrial activities tend to be very low and marked by poor technological development. Most of these countries have large quantities of surplus labour, considerable unemployment or underemployment and fairly high rates of population growth. Another common feature is inadequate infrastructure – poor road and transportation networks, a lack of sufficient irrigation, etc. Equally important are the underdevelopment of human resources in terms of skills and education and the weakness of economic and financial institutions.

Although a number of countries have made great strides in development since the United Nations (UN) classification was established in the 1940s, the list itself has remained practically unchanged (except for the addition of newly independent countries) since that time. As a result, certain countries – particularly in Asia and Latin America –

continue to be classified as developing countries, despite the fact that their economies may no longer qualify for that classification.

*Low-income countries* are those which had a per caput GNP of US$695 or less in 1993.

*Middle-income countries* are those which had a per caput GNP of more than US$695 but less than US$8 626 in 1993.

*High-income countries* are those which had a per caput GNP of US$8 626 or more in 1993.

*Least developed countries* are low-income countries suffering from long-term handicaps to growth, in particular low levels of human resource development and/or severe structural weakness (UN classification).

*Low-income food-deficit countries* are those which had a per caput GNP of US$1 345 or less in 1993 and a net deficit in cereal trade averaged over the preceding five marketing years.

### Symbols and units of measure

-  = none or negligible

...  = not available

0, 0.0  = zero or a quantity which is less than half of the unit shown

Billion  = 1 000 million

Tonnes  = metric tons

1969/71  = a crop, marketing or financial year running from one calendar year to the next

1969-71  = average for three calendar years

1969-71 to 1979-81 = the period from the first three-year average to the second three-year average

Figures in tables may not add up because of rounding.

# Abbreviations

ACC/SCN
Administrative Committee
on Coordination/Subcommittee
on Nutrition (United Nations)

BMI
Body mass index

BMR
Basal metabolic rate

CED
Chronic energy deficiency

CV
Coefficient of variation

DES
Dietary energy supply

GDP
Gross domestic product

GNP
Gross national product

HDI
Human development index

IFPRI
International Food Policy Research
Institute

LDCs
Least developed countries

LIFDCs
Low-income food-deficit countries

NCHS
National Center for Health
Statistics (United States)

SD
Standard deviation

UN
United Nations

UNDP
United Nations Development
Programme

UNU
United Nations University

WHO
World Health Organization

# Introduction

·

## Survey structure

·

## Food inadequacy and anthropometry

*The Fifth World Food Survey* reviewed the world food situation up to the early 1980s. Since then, much has changed on the world economic scene. With the collapse of communism, the so-called transition economies have emerged in Eastern Europe and the former USSR; a group of newly industrializing countries has begun to emerge in East and Southeast Asia; and many countries in Latin America and the Caribbean and Africa have been through a difficult period owing to a combination of debt crises, falling commodity prices, the rigours of stabilization and structural adjustment programmes and, in many cases, drought and war. At the same time, the spate of new breakthroughs that were being made in agricultural technology in the 1960s and 1970s appear to have waned in the 1980s, while environmental degradation has emerged as a major concern. All these changes have potential consequences for the supply and distribution of food around the world, with implications for the nutritional well-being of its inhabitants.

*The Sixth World Food Survey* attempts to review the emerging situation of food and nutrition in the world as a whole and in its various regions. The latest period assessed is the triennium 1990-92 but, where possible, comparisons are made with earlier periods – specifically, the triennia 1969-71 and 1979-81 – in order to analyse the pattern of change over time. Three major issues are covered in this survey: i) trends in the availability, regional distribution and composition of food supply in the world; ii) trends in the nutrition situation of the developing countries as assessed by different measures of food inadequacy; and iii) the anthropometric assessment of the nutritional status of people in the developing countries.

This introductory chapter gives a brief outline of the structure and contents of the survey before clarifying certain concepts that figure prominently in later chapters, which refer to estimates of food inadequacy, undernutrition and the assessment of nutritional status. These terms relate to the food and nutrition situation of a population, and an attempt is made here to explain what they mean and how they relate to or differ from each other, so as to help readers interpret the numerical estimates offered in this report.

As indicated above, the latest period of assessment in this survey is 1990-92 and the analyses focus on the long-term changes that occurred during the previous two decades. In the future it is planned to issue world food survey updates on a regular basis so as to reflect new data and short-term changes in food supply levels and the prevalence of food inadequacy or undernutrition.

1

## SURVEY STRUCTURE

Chapter 1 covers the trends in the availability, regional distribution and composition of aggregate food supplies. It presents an analysis of how the per caput availability of dietary energy supply, proteins and fats evolved in the two decades preceding 1990-92. The analysis is made for the world as a whole as well as for separate regions and leads to a discussion of the distribution of food supplies among different regions of the world, including how this distribution has been changing over time. Finally, changes in the food supply composition are discussed, involving issues such as the relative importance of different food groups (i.e. vegetable products and animal products) in total food supplies, the nature of diversification in food consumption patterns and the changing importance of staple foods.

Chapter 2 presents estimates of food inadequacy in the world and its different regions. By comparing the distribution of dietary energy supply (DES) with per caput energy requirements in different countries, two types of food inadequacy measures are provided, namely the *prevalence* and the *intensity* of food inadequacy. The prevalence measure is concerned with the proportion and number of people who have inadequate access to food, i.e. those whose access falls short of a specified cutoff point. The previous world food surveys also presented prevalence estimates for earlier periods but the present survey offers, for the first time, estimates of the intensity of food inadequacy. The objective of this new measure is to assess by how far access to food falls short of requirements. This shortfall is measured from two different perspectives: in terms of the underfed and in terms of the country as a whole. The former perspective indicates the extent of deprivation of the underfed or undernourished population; the latter is meant to shed light on the seriousness of the challenge facing a country if all its people are to have adequate access to food.

Chapter 3 complements the analysis of Chapter 2 by presenting anthropometric assessments of nutritional status. The nature of available data on the distribution of food supplies is such that the food inadequacy approach can only deal with populations as a whole and not specific population groups such as children, adolescents and adults. Information on specific population groups is also of interest but requires a different approach; hence nutrition anthropometry is used for this purpose in Chapter 3. The coverage of developing countries is not as complete as in the preceding chapters. Global estimates of undernutrition, as assessed by anthropometry, can only be provided for children under five years of age and for a limited number of developing countries, as the source drawn on was the World Health Organization's Global Database on Child Growth. For adults and adolescents, the coverage is even more limited. Nonetheless, an advance is made by presenting some estimates for adults who were typically left out of past anthropometric assessments. Nutritionists and others have recently begun to accept the so-called body mass index (BMI) as a satisfactory indicator for adults, while a growing number of anthropometric studies are generating data on adult height and weight measurements. This has made it possible to present more systematic evidence on adult nutritional status in parts of the developing world.

Chapter 4 concludes the survey by reiterating salient findings of the preceding chapters and by making observations on the relationships between different indicators of deprivation. Food inadequacy and anthropometric measures both try to capture, in different ways, the phenomenon of nutritional deprivation. Both indicators are fundamentally different, as explained below, and thus cannot be expected to give similar estimates of the number of people who are nutritionally deprived. Instead, they must be seen as complementing each other. For comparisons across countries, more general indicators of deprivation, such as per caput gross domestic product (GDP) and the human development index (HDI) values are included. In countries where a large proportion of the population suffers from nutritional deprivation, one would generally expect a low level of human development.

The main body of the survey is followed by four appendixes. The first presents the country composition of the regional aggregates and economic groups used in this report. Appendix 2 comprises a main table containing relevant data on individual countries and some auxiliary tables. Appendix 3 provides a detailed discussion of the methodology underlying the estimation of food inadequacy, the results of which are presented in Chapter 2, while Appendix 4 deals with methodologies related to the anthropometric assessment of nutritional status presented in Chapter 3.

3

## FOOD INADEQUACY AND ANTHROPOMETRY

The concern with undernutrition underpins much of this survey. Two kinds of undernutrition indicators are used: food inadequacy and physical growth and development indices. In order to interpret correctly the estimates based on these indicators, it is necessary to understand the extent to which the indicators can capture the underlying concept and how they themselves are related. With that objective in view, a discussion of the relationship between food inadequacy and anthropometry is presented here.

### Undernutrition and food inadequacy

The concept of food inadequacy, as defined in this survey, is very close to the concept of undernutrition. Both refer to energy deficiency relative to requirement norms; however, they are not identical. Owing to this conceptual difference as well as some methodological compromises enforced by the limitations of knowledge, the estimated prevalence of food inadequacy will diverge from the actual prevalence of undernutrition, even leaving aside the problem of measurement errors. Following is an explanation of some of the main reasons for this divergence.

i) The role of general health and the incidence of infectious diseases in the aetiology of undernutrition can affect the prevalence of food inadequacy. One consequence of infection is to raise the dietary energy requirements of the body. This is because extra energy is needed to fight infection and enable the body to recover from the damage done, and also because increased food losses may occur owing to malabsorption in the case of gastrointestinal diseases. Since the incidence and severity of infection vary depending on a multiplicity of factors such as the hygiene and sanitation of a particular environment, traditional practices of personal hygiene and access to both preventive and curative health care, dietary energy requirements will also vary according to the same factors.

Ideally, food adequacy should be assessed relative to different energy requirements associated with different environments of health and hygiene. In practice, this is difficult to do, as it requires a detailed knowledge of the disease environments of each region and of the effects they might have on energy requirements – such knowledge simply does not exist at present. As a result, the methodology of estimating energy requirements usually makes the simplified assumption of a satisfactory environment of health and hygiene. The present survey departs from the standard practice by allowing for recovery from frequent bouts of infection in the estimated energy requirements of children. This leaves out adolescents and adults, however, and even for children the allowance may not be adequate for particularly severe conditions. Therefore, it is very likely that the energy requirements calculated for different regions of the developing world fail to allow fully for the effects of infection. To that extent, the assessment of food inadequacy presented may well underestimate the true prevalence of undernutrition.

ii) Another reason why the presence of infection may cause a divergence between the prevalence of food inadequacy and undernutrition is that, in cases of severe infection, the body may not be able to absorb the dietary energy that is ingested as food, and sometimes (as in the case of anorexia) the infected person may already have a lower than normal food intake. Repeated infections over a long period of time will make a person undernourished even if his or her access to food is

4

adequate for a healthy and active life. In this event, the prevalence of food inadequacy will necessarily underestimate the prevalence of undernutrition.

iii) A potential source of divergence which may lead instead to an overestimation of the prevalence of undernutrition is the methodology, adopted in this survey, based on the assumption that each individual has a fixed requirement of dietary energy. If a person's access to food is consistently below this fixed level, he or she will be unable to maintain his or her body weight or physical activity. It is thus argued that, if the daily energy intake is below the optimal level required for a balance of energy or stable body weight and for sustaining a socially desirable level of activity, a person is undernourished. On the other hand, some would argue that there may be a range of variation in energy requirements, which reflect a metabolic adaptation to a lower daily energy intake at little or no cost in terms of reduced body weight and activity. In this case, a person is said to "adapt" to a low level of daily energy intake and is therefore not deemed to be undernourished. Thus, the methodology which estimates food inadequacy based on fixed energy requirements may overestimate the prevalence of undernutrition.

The magnitude of any such overestimation in the present survey is likely to be rather small. First, although the relevant knowledge is still incomplete, it is believed that the range of metabolic adaptation that entails little or no cost is probably very small. Second, the methodology adopted bases energy requirements on the *minimum* levels of body weight and physical activity observed among healthy individuals.[1] These minimum levels refer to the lower end of the range of interindividual variations (in body weight and activity) and not directly to the possibility of metabolic adaptation by a person, but it seems unlikely that individuals could adapt without any risk to health and function below these minimum levels. Consequently, if there is any overestimation of undernutrition in this survey, it is small.

## Undernutrition and anthropometry

The claim of anthropometry as an indicator of undernutrition is that it can determine whether or not a person is in good health by judging his or her weight and height against the normal range of weights and heights of a healthy population.[2] Certain points need to be clarified regarding this claim.

---

[1] The reason for this is explained in Appendix 3.

[2] This detailed methodology and its logic are explained in Appendix 4.

Undernutrition occurs as a result of inadequate access to and utilization of dietary energy by the body. Regardless of whether utilization is inadequate because food intake is low or because the body is unable to absorb energy owing to the effects of disease, the results of low utilization will be reflected in the dimensions of the body – in the form of either low height or low weight or both. Therefore, to the extent that weight and height measurements indicate the presence or absence of undernutrition, whether it be owing to a lack of food, to disease or both, anthropometry provides a fairly comprehensive measure of undernutrition. However, it leaves out an important dimension. Undernutrition has been defined as a state of dietary energy deficiency whereby an individual is unable to maintain good health (in the sense of being free from avoidable morbidity, risk of premature mortality, etc.) or a desirable level of physical activity. An anthropometric assessment cannot provide information on whether an individual is capable of maintaining a desirable level of physical activity. A state of dietary energy deficiency may manifest itself by keeping physical activity at a low level in order to maintain an energy balance. Anthropometry cannot capture this particular manifestation and may therefore tend to underestimate the prevalence of undernutrition. However, if people behaved in such a way that, when faced with dietary energy stress, they first allowed their physical dimensions to adjust before reducing their activity, anthropometry would correctly capture the whole set of undernourished population. Unfortunately, there is no convincing evidence that people consistently behave in this way, i.e. giving priority to physical activity over physical dimensions. Consequently, anthropometric assessments will generally underestimate the prevalence of undernutrition, and this point should be kept in mind when interpreting the anthropometric estimates of nutritional deprivation.

### Food inadequacy and nutritional anthropometry

The preceding discussion suggests that neither the food inadequacy approach nor the anthropometric assessment approach can fully capture the phenomenon of undernutrition. Each captures different aspects, so estimates of undernutrition based on them will inevitably differ. It is also evident that each approach has its own strengths and weaknesses. It is therefore necessary to use them in tandem so as to allow as complete an assessment of nutritional deprivation as possible. Such is the strategy adopted in this survey.

It is also interesting to note that the two approaches have certain methodological features in common: both rely on data containing unknown measurement errors; both employ anthropometric measurements to calculate daily energy requirements, in the case of the food adequacy approach, and to generate proxy indicators of nutritional status, in the anthropometric approach; and both apply analytical methods that essentially generate probability estimates of the number of people at risk either of having inadequate access to food or of being undernourished.

# CHAPTER 1

# Trends in availability and composition of food supplies

•

Trends in dietary energy supply

•

DES growth in relation
to population growth

•

Trends in availability of dietary
protein and fats

•

Distribution of food in the world

•

Changes in food composition

This chapter presents an analysis of the availability and composition of food in the world, both globally and by region.[3] Trends in the per caput availability of dietary energy, proteins and fats are discussed, as are the distribution of food among different parts of the world and the changing patterns of food consumption in both developed and developing countries. The basic data for this analysis are derived from the food balance sheets compiled every year by FAO with country-level data on the production and trade of food commodities.[4] Using these data and the available information on seed rates, waste coefficients, stock changes and types of utilization (feed, food, other uses), a supply/utilization account is prepared for each commodity in weight terms. The food component, which is usually derived as a balancing item, refers to the total amount of the commodity available for human consumption during the year. Besides commodity-by-commodity information, the FAO food balance sheets also provide total food availability estimates by aggregating the food component of all commodities after conversion into nutritive values. From these values and the available population estimates, the per caput dietary energy, protein and fat supplies, which form the basis of the analysis in this chapter, are derived.

In attempting to obtain a consistent estimate of food supply within a specified year, certain difficulties are faced when matching the reference periods of trade and agricultural production data and when estimating annual changes in stocks. However, the effect of possible errors owing to these difficulties can be reduced if the analysis of food supply is based on averages of two or more years. As in the past, the present world food survey is based on three-year averages, with information covering the most recent period for which data are available, i.e. 1990-92, as well as 1969-71 and 1979-81 in order to indicate the broad trends. The survey covers 98 developing countries and 31 developed countries (countries with a population of less than one million were excluded).

## TRENDS IN DIETARY ENERGY SUPPLY

Worldwide, per caput dietary energy supply (DES) increased by 11 percent – from 2 440 to 2 720 kcal/day – during the 21-year period between 1969-71 and 1990-92 (Table 1). This translates into an average annual growth rate of about 0.5 percent over the two decades. It is worth

9

---

[3] The country composition of the regional aggregates and economic groups is presented in Appendix 1.
[4] These annual statistics are published occasionally as three-year averages, e.g. *FAO Food Balance Sheets, 1984-86 average*, published in 1991.

noting several aspects of this overall performance, some of which signify positive achievements and others which do not. The positive achievements can be enumerated as follows:

- First and foremost these figures indicate that, in the world as a whole, food production has continued to outstrip population growth, although not universally so.
- Second, the developing countries as a group have continued to increase their per caput DES at a faster rate than the developed countries in spite of experiencing a much higher rate of population growth. In the 1980s, for example, the annual average growth rate of per caput DES was 0.7 percent in the developing countries as against 0.2 percent in the developed countries (Table 1). This was partly because the former had started from a much lower base, but it may also be a reflection of the fact that, owing to technological and other advances, they were able to make good use of available resources in an effort to keep ahead of population growth.

Against these positive achievements, one must also weigh two disconcerting developments: the worldwide slowdown in the growth of per caput DES and the absolute decline in per caput DES in large parts of the world.

- Both the developed and the developing regions experienced a slight slowdown in the growth of per caput DES in the 1980s compared with the 1970s – from 0.3 to 0.2 percent and from 0.9 to 0.7 percent, respectively (Table 1). There were, however, significant intraregional variations. In the developed world, the slowdown was exclusively confined to the transition economies where the annual growth rate in fact turned negative in the 1980s from a small but positive rate (0.2 percent) achieved in the 1970s. By contrast, the annual growth rate of per caput DES in the industrialized countries increased from 0.3 percent to 0.5 percent during the same period.

  There were also variations within the developing world. Considering the geographical classification first, the slowdown in the growth of per caput DES was confined mostly to East and Southeast Asia and the Latin American and Caribbean countries. Sub-Saharan Africa continued to experience a virtually unchanged negative growth, while South Asia emerged as an exception by experiencing a change from almost zero growth in the 1970s to an average annual rate of 0.9 percent in the 1980s (Table 1).

  The sharpest decelerations in annual growth in per caput DES were mostly confined to the two regions which had already attained a fairly high level of per caput DES by the end of the 1970s (the Near East and North Africa and Latin America and the Caribbean), while the countries in the "low-income" and "low-income food-deficit" groups on the whole maintained steady growth, as can be seen from Table 1. These countries either experienced a slight acceleration in the growth of per caput DES or maintained a steady growth. However, this is not true for all countries in these regions, especially those that belong to the group of least developed countries (LDCs).

• Even more disconcerting than the phenomenon of declining growth in per caput DES is that it failed to grow at all in many parts of the world, and, in some parts, even declined in absolute terms. Considering the two decades together, there was an absolute decline in per caput DES in sub-Saharan Africa and the transition economies and stagnation in the LDCs as a whole (Table 1). The problem seems

## TABLE 1

### PER CAPUT DES BY REGION AND ECONOMIC GROUP, 1969-71, 1979-81 AND 1990-92

| Region/economic group | Per caput DES | | | Average annual rate of increase | |
|---|---|---|---|---|---|
| | 1969-71 | 1979-81 | 1990-92 | 1969-71 to 1979-81 | 1979-81 to 1990-92 |
| | | (kcal/day) | | | (Percentage) |
| **Developed countries** | 3 190 | 3 280 | 3 350 | 0.3 | 0.2 |
| Industrialized countries | 3 120 | 3 220 | 3 410 | 0.3 | 0.5 |
| Transition economies | 3 330 | 3 400 | 3 230 | 0.2 | -0.5 |
| **Developing countries** | 2 140 | 2 330 | 2 520 | 0.9 | 0.7 |
| Latin America and the Caribbean | 2 510 | 2 720 | 2 740 | 0.8 | 0.0 |
| Sub-Saharan Africa | 2 140 | 2 080 | 2 040 | -0.3 | -0.2 |
| Near East and North Africa | 2 380 | 2 850 | 2 960 | 1.8 | 0.3 |
| East and Southeast Asia | 2 060 | 2 370 | 2 680 | 1.4 | 1.1 |
| South Asia | 2 060 | 2 070 | 2 290 | 0.0 | 0.9 |
| **Economic groups of developing countries** | | | | | |
| Least developed | 2 060 | 2 040 | 2 040 | -0.1 | 0.0 |
| Low-income food-deficit | 2 060 | 2 230 | 2 450 | 0.8 | 0.8 |
| Low-income | 2 060 | 2 210 | 2 430 | 0.7 | 0.9 |
| Middle-income | 2 360 | 2 670 | 2 760 | 1.2 | 0.3 |
| **World** | 2 440 | 2 580 | 2 720 | 0.5 | 0.5 |

to have become endemic in sub-Saharan Africa, where the per caput DES declined in each of the two decades, whereas for the transition economies the decline was more marked in the 1980s. The same decade also brought stagnation to the indebted Latin American and Caribbean countries, which had done reasonably well in the preceding decade.

Once again, it needs to be emphasized that what is true for group averages is not necessarily true for each individual country within the group. Performance varied significantly even among countries within regional groups.

Table 2 lists the top five and bottom five countries within the developing world as judged by the growth of per caput DES achieved in the two decades between 1969-71 and 1990-92. Each of the top five countries (Algeria, Saudi Arabia, Tunisia, Lebanon and the Syrian Arab Republic) achieved growth rates in excess of 1.5 percent per annum, which is three times the world average of 0.5 percent, while the bottom five countries (the Central African Republic, Afghanistan, Liberia, Malawi and Peru) suffered a negative annual growth rate of between -1 and -1.5 percent.

## DES GROWTH IN RELATION TO POPULATION GROWTH

This analysis has so far been concerned with the level and growth of per caput DES which is the result of two separate trends, one involving total DES and the other involving population. Since these need not move in the same direction, it would be useful to consider them separately and look at their relationship so as to give a clearer picture of how the trends in per caput DES came about. The relevant figures are presented in Table 3.

**TABLE 2**

| TOP FIVE AND BOTTOM FIVE DEVELOPING COUNTRIES IN TERMS OF PER CAPUT DES GROWTH RATES, 1969-71 TO 1990-92 | | | |
|---|---|---|---|
| **Average annual rate of increase** | | | |
| Top five countries | | Bottom five countries | |
| (Percentage) | | | |
| Algeria | 2.2 | Central African Rep. | -1.5 |
| Saudi Arabia | 1.8 | Afghanistan | -1.3 |
| Tunisia | 1.7 | Liberia | -1.1 |
| Lebanon | 1.6 | Malawi | -1.0 |
| Syrian Arab Rep. | 1.5 | Peru | -1.0 |

**TABLE 3**

## DES AND POPULATION GROWTH BY REGION AND ECONOMIC GROUP, 1969-71 TO 1979-81 AND 1979-81 TO 1990-92

| Region/economic group | Average annual rate of increase | | |
|---|---|---|---|
| | DES | Population | Per caput DES |
| | | (Percentage) | |
| **Developed countries** | | | |
| 1969-71 to 1979-81 | 1.1 | 0.8 | 0.3 |
| 1979-81 to 1990-92 | 0.9 | 0.7 | 0.2 |
| Industrialized countries | | | |
| 1969-71 to 1979-81 | 1.1 | 0.8 | 0.3 |
| 1979-81 to 1990-92 | 1.2 | 0.7 | 0.5 |
| Transition economies | | | |
| 1969-71 to 1979-81 | 1.1 | 0.9 | 0.2 |
| 1979-81 to 1990-92 | 0.2 | 0.7 | -0.5 |
| **Developing countries** | | | |
| 1969-71 to 1979-81 | 3.1 | 2.2 | 0.9 |
| 1979-81 to 1990-92 | 2.8 | 2.1 | 0.7 |
| Latin America and the Caribbean | | | |
| 1969-71 to 1979-81 | 3.2 | 2.4 | 0.8 |
| 1979-81 to 1990-92 | 2.1 | 2.1 | 0.0 |
| Sub-Saharan Africa | | | |
| 1969-71 to 1979-81 | 2.6 | 2.9 | -0.3 |
| 1979-81 to 1990-92 | 2.9 | 3.1 | -0.2 |
| Near East and North Africa | | | |
| 1969-71 to 1979-81 | 4.5 | 2.7 | 1.8 |
| 1979-81 to 1990-92 | 3.1 | 2.8 | 0.3 |
| East and Southeast Asia | | | |
| 1969-71 to 1979-81 | 3.4 | 2.0 | 1.4 |
| 1979-81 to 1990-92 | 2.7 | 1.6 | 1.1 |
| South Asia | | | |
| 1969-71 to 1979-81 | 2.3 | 2.3 | 0.0 |
| 1979-81 to 1990-92 | 3.1 | 2.2 | 0.9 |
| **Economic groups of developing countries** | | | |
| Least developed | | | |
| 1969-71 to 1979-81 | 2.5 | 2.4 | -0.1 |
| 1979-81 to 1990-92 | 2.6 | 2.6 | 0.0 |
| Low-income food-deficit | | | |
| 1969-71 to 1979-81 | 3.0 | 2.2 | 0.8 |
| 1979-81 to 1990-92 | 2.9 | 2.1 | 0.8 |
| Low-income | | | |
| 1969-71 to 1979-81 | 2.8 | 2.1 | 0.7 |
| 1979-81 to 1990-92 | 2.9 | 2.0 | 0.9 |
| Middle-income | | | |
| 1969-71 to 1979-81 | 3.7 | 2.5 | 1.2 |
| 1979-81 to 1990-92 | 2.5 | 2.2 | 0.3 |
| **World** | | | |
| 1969-71 to 1979-81 | 2.4 | 1.9 | 0.5 |
| 1979-81 to 1990-92 | 2.2 | 1.7 | 0.5 |

It was noted earlier that global per caput DES grew at a more or less constant rate in the two decades under consideration. It can now be seen that this constancy was the result of a mutually offsetting deceleration in the growth of food supplies and population. In other words, the growth of world food supplies slowed down over time – from an annual rate of 2.4 percent in the 1970s to 2.2 percent in the 1980s – and, despite this slowdown, a constant rate of growth in per caput DES was maintained because population growth also slowed down correspondingly from 1.9 to 1.7 percent per annum. This offsetting slowdown in the growth of DES and population is also evident in most of the broad regions but there are some notable variations in pattern.

- In the transition economies, the growth of DES slowed down more than population growth, resulting in negative growth of per caput DES in the 1980s.
- The LDCs, and especially the countries of sub-Saharan Africa, experienced the opposite phenomenon of high DES growth being offset by high population growth. Contrary to the overall trend, both the DES and the population grew faster in the second decade in these regions but DES growth was again offset by population growth. Thus, although both the transition economies and sub-Saharan Africa experienced negative growth in per caput DES in the 1980s, this was explained by different sets of forces in each case.
- South Asia and, to a lesser extent, the industrialized world, diverged from the overall pattern of DES and population growth. In these regions, the rate of DES growth accelerated while population growth declined, thus producing a higher rate of growth in per caput DES in the 1980s compared with the 1970s.

The analysis of DES growth in relation to population growth throws an interesting light on the comparative experiences of South Asia and sub-Saharan Africa – the two most impoverished regions of the world. In the two decades whether taken together or separately, these regions did not differ much in terms of growth of aggregate DES but, in South Asia, population growth was lower and declining while, in sub-Saharan Africa, it was higher and on the rise (Table 3). As a result, per caput DES rose in South Asia, especially in the 1980s, while it declined in sub-Saharan Africa in both decades.

In addition to relating DES growth to population growth, it is useful to relate DES growth with initial levels of per caput DES. The higher the initial level, the more difficult it is to achieve a given rate of growth. This means that a low rate of growth at higher levels of per caput DES is a qualitatively different phenomenon from slow growth at lower initial levels; it is necessary to distinguish between the two in order to identify the nature of constraints affecting per caput DES growth. A proper analysis requires the classification of countries according to initial levels of per caput DES and population growth. Such a two-way classification according to the initial per caput DES level was made, taking 2 500 kcal/day as the dividing line on the grounds that no developed country has a per caput DES below this level (see Appendix 2), while the classification according to population growth was made with 2 percent per annum as the dividing line.

A comparison of per caput DES growth rates of developing countries classified in this manner produces the following results (Table 4): A few countries experienced slow growth in per caput DES despite having relatively low rates of population growth as well as low initial levels of per caput DES. Prime examples are Haiti, Afghanistan and Cambodia, where the per caput DES actually declined over the two decades. At the opposite end of the scale, a few countries (notably Mexico, Egypt and Turkey) registered relatively high rates of growth in per caput DES, despite experiencing a high initial per caput DES and high rate of population growth.

15

TABLE 4

**DISTRIBUTION OF 98 DEVELOPING COUNTRIES BY PER CAPUT DES IN 1969-71 AND ITS GROWTH FROM 1969-71 TO 1990-92, AND BY POPULATION GROWTH**

| Per caput DES 1969-71: | ≤2 500 kcal/day | | | | >2500 kcal/day | | | |
|---|---|---|---|---|---|---|---|---|
| Annual population growth rate, 1969-71 to 1990-92: | >2% | | ≤2% | | >2% | | ≤2% | |
| Per caput DES annual growth rate, 1969-71 to 1990-92: | ≤0.5% | >0.5% | ≤0.5% | >0.5% | ≤0.5% | >0.5% | ≤0.5% | >0.5% |
| | *(Number of countries)* | | | | | | | |
| Developing countries | 45 | 28 | 5 | 6 | 3 | 3 | 5 | 3 |
| Latin America and the Caribbean | 7 | 5 | 2 | 2 | 1 | 1 | 5 | 1 |
| Sub-Saharan Africa | 31 | 7 | 0 | 1 | 0 | 0 | 0 | 0 |
| Near East and North Africa | 1 | 9 | 1 | 1 | 2 | 2 | 0 | 0 |
| East and Southeast Asia | 4 | 4 | 1 | 2 | 0 | 0 | 0 | 2 |
| South Asia | 2 | 2 | 1 | 0 | 0 | 0 | 0 | 0 |
| **Economic groups of developing countries** | | | | | | | | |
| Least developed | 23 | 8 | 3 | 0 | 0 | 0 | 0 | 0 |
| Low-income food-deficit | 37 | 18 | 4 | 2 | 0 | 1 | 0 | 0 |
| Low-income | 32 | 9 | 5 | 1 | 0 | 1 | 0 | 0 |
| Middle-income | 13 | 19 | 0 | 5 | 3 | 2 | 5 | 3 |

TABLE 5

**TOTAL AND ANIMAL PROTEIN SUPPLIES BY REGION AND ECONOMIC GROUP,
1969-71, 1979-81 AND 1990-92**

| Region/economic group | Total protein | | | Animal protein | | |
|---|---|---|---|---|---|---|
| | 1969-71 | 1979-81 | 1990-92 | 1969-71 | 1979-81 | 1990-92 |
| | *(g/per caput/day)* | | | | | |
| Developed countries | 95 | 99 | 102 | 51 | 56 | 59 |
| Industrialized countries | 93 | 97 | 103 | 54 | 58 | 63 |
| Transition economies | 100 | 103 | 100 | 44 | 51 | 51 |
| Developing countries | 53 | 57 | 62 | 10 | 12 | 15 |
| Latin America and the Caribbean | 65 | 68 | 68 | 25 | 29 | 29 |
| Sub-Saharan Africa | 54 | 51 | 49 | 11 | 12 | 10 |
| Near East and North Africa | 66 | 77 | 80 | 14 | 18 | 18 |
| East and Southeast Asia | 49 | 56 | 65 | 7 | 9 | 16 |
| South Asia | 51 | 50 | 55 | 7 | 7 | 10 |
| Economic groups of developing countries | | | | | | |
| Least developed | 52 | 51 | 50 | 10 | 10 | 9 |
| Low-income food-deficit | 50 | 53 | 59 | 8 | 9 | 12 |
| Low-income | 51 | 53 | 59 | 7 | 8 | 12 |
| Middle-income | 59 | 66 | 69 | 18 | 21 | 23 |
| World | 65 | 68 | 71 | 22 | 23 | 25 |

## TRENDS IN AVAILABILITY OF DIETARY PROTEIN AND FATS

As changes in food supply levels are usually accompanied by modifications in food consumption patterns, the changes in protein and fat supply levels can differ to a certain extent from those in energy supply. Specific information on dietary protein and fats for 1969-71, 1979-81 and 1990-92 is presented in Tables 5 and 6.

As in the case of DES, per caput protein and fat supplies in the world as a whole increased steadily in the two decades from 1969-71. The same pattern of steady increases is also observed for the broad groupings of developed and developing countries. However, variations in this pattern

**TABLE 6**

## TOTAL AND ANIMAL FAT SUPPLIES BY REGION AND ECONOMIC GROUP, 1969-71, 1979-81 AND 1990-92

| Region/economic group | Total fats | | | Animal fats | | |
|---|---|---|---|---|---|---|
| | 1969-71 | 1979-81 | 1990-92 | 1969-71 | 1979-81 | 1990-92 |
| | *(g/per caput/day)* | | | | | |
| Developed countries | 108 | 118 | 125 | 68 | 73 | 73 |
| Industrialized countries | 117 | 127 | 138 | 72 | 75 | 76 |
| Transition economies | 89 | 100 | 98 | 61 | 69 | 67 |
| Developing countries | 33 | 40 | 51 | 12 | 15 | 19 |
| Latin America and the Caribbean | 57 | 71 | 78 | 30 | 34 | 34 |
| Sub-Saharan Africa | 41 | 42 | 41 | 9 | 10 | 9 |
| Near East and North Africa | 50 | 65 | 70 | 18 | 22 | 20 |
| East and Southeast Asia | 25 | 33 | 51 | 10 | 14 | 24 |
| South Asia | 29 | 32 | 41 | 8 | 8 | 11 |
| Economic groups of developing countries | | | | | | |
| Least developed | 31 | 31 | 32 | 9 | 9 | 8 |
| Low-income food-deficit | 29 | 35 | 46 | 10 | 12 | 18 |
| Low-income | 28 | 34 | 45 | 9 | 12 | 18 |
| Middle-income | 46 | 58 | 68 | 20 | 23 | 24 |
| World | 55 | 61 | 69 | 28 | 30 | 32 |

17

begin to emerge as soon as the analysis is disaggregated into smaller groupings.

In the developing regions, changes in per caput protein supplies seem to have followed four broad patterns. In sub-Saharan Africa per caput protein supply declined in each of the two decades, which parallels the decrease in that region's per caput energy supply. In Latin America and the Caribbean and the Near East and North Africa positive gains were made in the 1970s but this momentum was lost in the 1980s. In East and Southeast Asia increases occurred in both decades. Finally, in South Asia the supplies remained constant in the 1970s and then increased in the 1980s.

The patterns of change in per caput fat supply are similar to those of protein supply but with the following differences: first, in sub-Saharan Africa, per caput fat supply remained constant over the two decades instead of declining in absolute terms as did the per caput protein supply; second, the acceleration in the growth of per caput fat supply in Asia occurred in the 1980s, not only in East and Southeast Asia (as in the case of protein) but also in South Asia.

Considering the dietary energy, protein and fat contents of aggregate food supplies, and on the basis of the experience of the two decades from 1969-71 to 1990-92, it is possible to distinguish three regional groupings in the developing world:

i) Sub-Saharan Africa, which experienced absolute declines in per caput energy and protein supplies but a constant per caput fat supply.
ii) Latin America and the Caribbean and the Near East and North Africa, where strong growth in the 1970s turned into either much slower growth or complete stagnation in the 1980s with respect to per caput dietary, protein and fat supplies.
iii) East, Southeast and South Asia, where steady or accelerated increases in per caput dietary energy, protein and fat supplies occurred in the 1980s.

## DISTRIBUTION OF FOOD IN THE WORLD

As a result of various changes in the availability of food in different parts of the world, the distribution of food among regions and countries as well as the disparities between different parts of the world are changing over time. This section attempts to delineate some of the changes.

During 1990-92 the developing regions, which contained 76 percent of the world's population, had access to 71 percent of the world's DES, 66 percent of its protein supply and 57 percent of its fat supply (Figure 1). The disparity between the two parts of the world is obviously much sharper with respect to protein and fat supplies than with respect to energy for the simple reason that protein-rich and fatty foods are normally more expensive than basic energy-rich foods. Nevertheless, the difference in per caput DES is still quite large. As can be seen from Table 1, per caput DES in the developed world was 3 350 kcal in 1990-92 compared with 2 520 kcal in the developing countries, i.e. the average person in the developed world consumed one-third more calories than the average person in the developing world.

Since considerable disparities exist within both the developed and developing regions, the data were disaggregated further so as to present a clearer picture of the distribution of per caput DES. The developed regions were divided into industrialized countries and the transition economies (i.e. the former USSR and the East European countries), while the developing regions were classified as the LDCs and others (for details of classification, see Appendix 1). The distribution of food and population for 1990-92 in these four regions is shown in Figure 2. The industrialized countries' share of the world's DES was far in excess of its population share, while the opposite was true for the LDCs. The

**FIGURE 1**

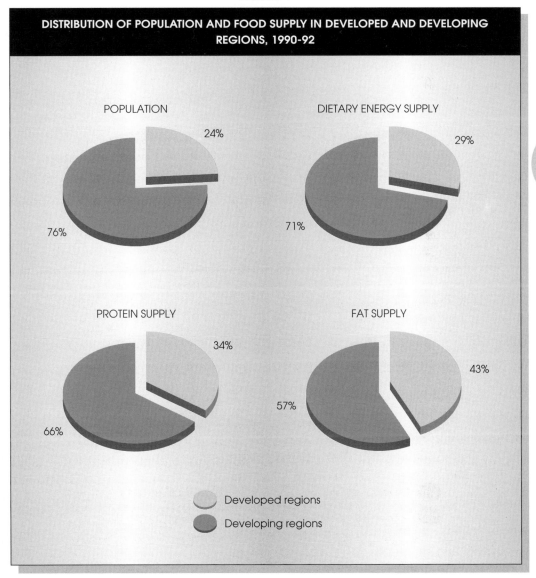

DISTRIBUTION OF POPULATION AND FOOD SUPPLY IN DEVELOPED AND DEVELOPING REGIONS, 1990-92

POPULATION

24%

76%

DIETARY ENERGY SUPPLY

29%

71%

PROTEIN SUPPLY

34%

66%

FAT SUPPLY

43%

57%

Developed regions
Developing regions

19

remaining two groups' shares of DES and population were fairly close to each other.

The disparity in per caput DES between the richest and poorest parts of the world becomes much more pronounced at this lower level of aggregation. Whereas the average person in the developed regions as a whole consumed one-third more calories than his or her counterpart in

**FIGURE 2**

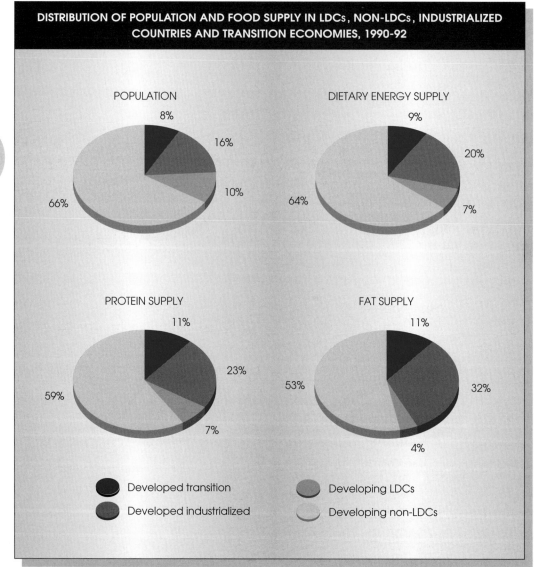

**DISTRIBUTION OF POPULATION AND FOOD SUPPLY IN LDCs, NON-LDCs, INDUSTRIALIZED COUNTRIES AND TRANSITION ECONOMIES, 1990-92**

POPULATION
8%
16%
10%
66%

DIETARY ENERGY SUPPLY
9%
20%
7%
64%

PROTEIN SUPPLY
11%
23%
7%
59%

FAT SUPPLY
11%
32%
4%
53%

Developed transition

Developed industrialized

Developing LDCs

Developing non-LDCs

the developing regions in 1990-92, the average person in the industrialized countries consumed two-thirds more calories than his or her counterpart in the LDCs. If account were to be taken of disparities in available food supplies among individuals within countries, undoubtedly the most privileged would be found to be consuming a multiple of the amount of calories consumed by the poor.

The LDCs lagged way behind even in comparison with the more privileged parts of the developing world. Thus, for example, the average person in the so-called middle-income countries of the developing world consumed just over one-third more calories than the average person in the LDCs (Table 1).

As a result of widely different changes in the availability of food in the world, the gap between the richest and poorest countries has become wider over time (Figure 3). Widening gaps are observed both between the developed and developing regions and within the developing world itself.

**FIGURE 3**

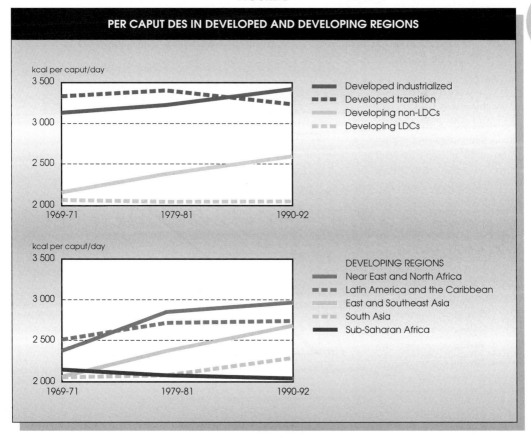

PER CAPUT DES IN DEVELOPED AND DEVELOPING REGIONS

kcal per caput/day

Developed industrialized
Developed transition
Developing non-LDCs
Developing LDCs

DEVELOPING REGIONS
Near East and North Africa
Latin America and the Caribbean
East and Southeast Asia
South Asia
Sub-Saharan Africa

BOX 1

## FOOD SITUATION IN THE REPUBLICS OF THE FORMER USSR

FAO has made a preliminary attempt to assess the emerging food situation in the republics of the former USSR. The figure below is based on the estimates of per caput DES for the periods 1986-88 and 1989-91; these estimates do not include alcoholic beverages.

The republics can be grouped into three broad categories according to their per caput DES in 1986-88. The group with the lowest levels of per caput DES – about 2 700 to 2 800 kcal – comprised the Republics of Kyrgyzstan, Uzbekistan, Tajikistan, Turkmenistan, Azerbaijan and Armenia. The top group – with a per caput DES of more than 3 300 kcal – comprised the Republics of Georgia, Ukraine, Belarus and Moldova. The Republics of Kazakstan, Estonia, Latvia and Lithuania as well as the Russian Federation belonged to the middle group.

The major changes that occurred by 1989-91 can be summed up as follows:

- Two of the republics from the bottom group, Azerbaijan and Tajikistan, fell further to a per caput DES level of about 2 500 kcal.
- Among the republics of the middle group, Estonia experienced a sharp decline in per caput DES which fell to the levels of the bottom group.
- Within the erstwhile top group, Georgia slipped badly and joined the ranks of the middle group.

Overall, there was no upward movement in per caput DES; some republics within each group suffered a decline while others remained constant. The most serious situations were those of Azerbaijan and Tajikistan, where per caput DES declined from levels that were already low in relation to the rest of the region and not much above those of the developing world.

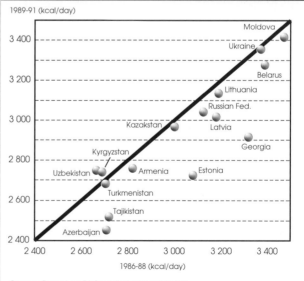

**PER CAPUT DES IN REPUBLICS OF THE FORMER USSR, 1986-88 AND 1989-91**

*Source:* Based on FAO preliminary estimates.

22

## CHANGES IN FOOD COMPOSITION

This section delineates the broad contours of changing food composition that are currently being observed in different regions. Three aspects are highlighted: the relative contribution of vegetable and animal products in total supplies of energy, protein and fats; the extent of food diversification observed in different parts of the world; and the changing importance of staple foods in aggregate food supplies.

In the world as a whole, the relative contribution of vegetable and animal products to total energy supplies remained remarkably stable throughout the 1970s and 1980s. The share of vegetable products, for example, stabilized at about 84 percent (Table 7). The same pattern is also observed for the developed countries, where the share of vegetable products stabilized at about 71 percent, although in the developing

TABLE 7

| Food group | World | | Developed countries | | Developing countries | |
|---|---|---|---|---|---|---|
| **SHARE OF MAJOR FOOD GROUPS IN TOTAL DES BY REGION AND ECONOMIC GROUP, 1969-71 AND 1990-92** | | | | | | |
| | 1969-71 | 1990-92 | 1969-71 | 1990-92 | 1969-71 | 1990-92 |
| | *(Percentage)* | | | | | |
| **Vegetable products** | 84.4 | 84.3 | 71.7 | 70.9 | 92.3 | 89.7 |
| Cereals | 50.1 | 51.2 | 32.6 | 30.4 | 60.9 | 59.6 |
| Sugar | 9.1 | 8.8 | 13.2 | 12.8 | 6.6 | 7.2 |
| Vegetable oils and fats | 5.7 | 8.2 | 8.2 | 11.1 | 4.1 | 7.0 |
| Roots and tubers | 7.5 | 5.0 | 5.0 | 3.8 | 9.0 | 5.4 |
| Vegetables and fruits | 4.2 | 4.3 | 4.5 | 4.9 | 4.5 | 4.8 |
| Pulses and nuts | 4.8 | 4.0 | 2.3 | 2.3 | 2.3 | 4.7 |
| Alcoholic beverages | 2.7 | 2.4 | 5.3 | 4.9 | 5.3 | 1.3 |
| Stimulants and spices | 0.4 | 0.4 | 0.4 | 0.6 | 0.4 | 0.4 |
| **Animal products** | 15.6 | 15.7 | 28.3 | 29.1 | 7.7 | 10.3 |
| Meat and offal | 6.4 | 7.4 | 11.1 | 12.8 | 3.5 | 5.2 |
| Milk | 4.8 | 4.3 | 8.9 | 8.6 | 2.2 | 2.6 |
| Animal oils and fats | 2.7 | 2.0 | 5.4 | 4.4 | 1.0 | 1.1 |
| Eggs | 0.8 | 0.9 | 1.5 | 1.8 | 0.3 | 0.7 |
| Fish | 0.9 | 1.0 | 1.4 | 1.3 | 0.6 | 0.7 |

(continued)

*(continued)*

**TABLE 7**

**SHARE OF MAJOR FOOD GROUPS IN TOTAL DES BY REGION AND ECONOMIC GROUP, 1969-71 AND 1990-92**

| Food group | Developed countries | | | | Developing countries | | | | | |
|---|---|---|---|---|---|---|---|---|---|---|
| | Industrialized | | Transition economies | | Least developed | | Low-income food-deficit | | Low-income | |
| | 1969-71 | 1990-92 | 1969-71 | 1990-92 | 1969-71 | 1990-92 | 1969-71 | 1990-92 | 1969-71 | 1990-92 |
| *(Percentage)* | | | | | | | | | | |
| **Vegetable products** | 69.6 | 70.2 | 75.6 | 72.4 | 93.4 | 94.0 | 93.7 | 90.8 | 93.9 | 90.7 |
| Cereals | 27.5 | 26.2 | 42.3 | 39.7 | 60.8 | 62.4 | 63.2 | 62.6 | 64.5 | 63.8 |
| Sugar | 13.9 | 13.1 | 11.8 | 12.3 | 4.3 | 3.5 | 5.5 | 6.1 | 5.0 | 5.6 |
| Vegetable oils and fats | 10.0 | 13.1 | 4.9 | 6.6 | 3.9 | 5.2 | 3.8 | 6.2 | 3.6 | 5.9 |
| Roots and tubers | 4.1 | 3.4 | 6.8 | 4.8 | 11.5 | 11.6 | 10.1 | 6.0 | 9.9 | 6.0 |
| Vegetables and fruits | 5.3 | 5.6 | 3.1 | 3.4 | 4.2 | 4.0 | 3.5 | 3.6 | 3.2 | 3.4 |
| Pulses and nuts | 2.6 | 2.8 | 1.7 | 1.1 | 6.7 | 5.7 | 6.5 | 4.8 | 6.5 | 4.6 |
| Alcoholic beverages | 5.5 | 5.3 | 4.9 | 4.2 | 1.4 | 1.1 | 0.9 | 1.1 | 0.9 | 1.1 |
| Stimulants and spices | 0.6 | 0.7 | 0.2 | 0.3 | 0.6 | 0.4 | 0.4 | 0.4 | 0.4 | 0.4 |
| **Animal products** | 30.4 | 29.8 | 24.4 | 27.6 | 6.6 | 6.0 | 6.3 | 9.2 | 6.1 | 9.3 |
| Meat and offal | 12.7 | 13.8 | 7.9 | 10.7 | 2.8 | 2.4 | 2.9 | 4.9 | 2.9 | 5.0 |
| Milk | 8.8 | 8.8 | 9.2 | 8.1 | 2.3 | 2.3 | 1.8 | 2.2 | 1.7 | 2.2 |
| Animal oils and fats | 5.5 | 3.9 | 5.2 | 5.3 | 0.7 | 0.5 | 0.8 | 1.0 | 0.8 | 1.0 |
| Eggs | 1.8 | 1.5 | 1.1 | 1.6 | 0.2 | 0.2 | 0.3 | 0.6 | 0.3 | 0.6 |
| Fish | 1.6 | 1.8 | 1.1 | 1.8 | 0.7 | 0.6 | 0.5 | 0.6 | 0.5 | 0.5 |

*(continued)*

countries there was a slight decline in the share of vegetable products and a corresponding increase in the share of animal products, from nearly 8 percent in 1969-71 to more than 10 percent in 1990-92.

There are, however, variations within each of these broad regions. In the developed regions, the share of animal products increased slightly in the transition economies, from approximately 24 to 28 percent. In the developing regions, the increased share of animal products was most evident in East and Southeast Asia, followed by South Asia and Latin American and Caribbean countries, whereas a similar increase did not occur in sub-Saharan Africa or countries of the Near East and North Africa. An increasing share of animal products in total DES is observed in both

(continued)

## TABLE 7

### SHARE OF MAJOR FOOD GROUPS IN TOTAL DES BY REGION AND ECONOMIC GROUP, 1969-71 AND 1990-92

| Food group | Developing regions | | | | | | | | | |
|---|---|---|---|---|---|---|---|---|---|---|
| | Latin America and Caribbean | | Sub-Saharan Africa | | Near East and North Africa | | East and Southeast Asia | | South Asia | |
| | 1969-71 | 1990-92 | 1969-71 | 1990-92 | 1969-71 | 1990-92 | 1969-71 | 1990-92 | 1969-71 | 1990-92 |
| | *(Percentage)* | | | | | | | | | |
| Vegetable products | 83.5 | 82.6 | 93.3 | 93.4 | 89.6 | 90.4 | 93.8 | 89.1 | 94.4 | 92.6 |
| Cereals | 39.4 | 38.4 | 43.7 | 44.7 | 61.1 | 56.9 | 67.7 | 66.5 | 67.0 | 64.5 |
| Sugar | 15.5 | 16.3 | 3.4 | 4.1 | 8.5 | 9.3 | 2.6 | 3.8 | 9.6 | 9.5 |
| Vegetable oils and fats | 6.0 | 11.1 | 6.4 | 8.0 | 7.3 | 10.6 | 2.4 | 5.1 | 4.3 | 6.8 |
| Roots and tubers | 7.2 | 4.1 | 21.7 | 21.0 | 1.3 | 2.2 | 12.2 | 5.1 | 1.8 | 1.6 |
| Vegetables and fruits | 6.0 | 5.2 | 6.0 | 5.6 | 7.1 | 7.0 | 2.8 | 3.3 | 2.8 | 3.0 |
| Pulses and nuts | 6.7 | 4.8 | 9.0 | 7.2 | 3.7 | 4.0 | 4.8 | 3.4 | 8.2 | 6.3 |
| Alcoholic beverages | 2.4 | 2.5 | 2.2 | 2.1 | 0.2 | 0.2 | 1.2 | 1.7 | 0.1 | 0.3 |
| Stimulants and spices | 0.3 | 0.3 | 0.8 | 0.6 | 0.4 | 0.4 | 0.1 | 0.2 | 0.6 | 0.6 |
| Animal products | 16.5 | 17.4 | 6.7 | 6.6 | 10.4 | 9.6 | 6.2 | 10.9 | 5.6 | 7.4 |
| Meat and offal | 8.1 | 8.4 | 3.0 | 2.9 | 3.2 | 3.3 | 4.0 | 7.7 | 0.9 | 1.1 |
| Milk | 5.2 | 5.4 | 2.3 | 2.4 | 4.7 | 3.9 | 0.3 | 0.5 | 3.2 | 4.5 |
| Animal oils and fats | 2.1 | 2.0 | 0.6 | 0.5 | 2.0 | 1.5 | 0.6 | 0.7 | 1.0 | 1.4 |
| Eggs | 0.6 | 1.0 | 0.2 | 0.2 | 0.3 | 0.6 | 0.5 | 1.0 | 0.1 | 0.2 |
| Fish | 0.5 | 0.5 | 0.6 | 0.7 | 0.2 | 0.3 | 0.8 | 1.0 | 0.3 | 0.3 |

low-income and low-income food-deficit countries, but not in the LDCs.

The situation regarding the sources of aggregate protein supplies is slightly different from that of aggregate energy supplies. The share of animal products in total protein supplies rose in both the developed and developing countries (Table 8). The same pattern is observed in both parts of the developed world – the industrialized countries and the transition economies – and also in all subgroups of the developing world, with the sole exception of sub-Saharan Africa where a rising share in the 1970s was completely offset by a decline in the 1980s. The most significant increase was observed in East and Southeast Asia, where the share of animal products in protein supplies increased from 15 percent in

TABLE 8

## SHARE OF MAJOR FOOD GROUPS IN TOTAL PROTEIN SUPPLIES BY REGION AND ECONOMIC GROUP, 1969-71 AND 1990-92

| Food group | World | | Developed countries | | Developing countries | |
|---|---|---|---|---|---|---|
| | 1969-71 | 1990-92 | 1969-71 | 1990-92 | 1969-71 | 1990-92 |
| | | | *(Percentage)* | | | |
| Vegetable products | 66.3 | 64.5 | 46.4 | 42.3 | 81.1 | 75.8 |
| Cereals | 46.3 | 47.2 | 32.2 | 29.0 | 56.8 | 56.2 |
| Pulses and nuts | 10.0 | 8.3 | 4.1 | 3.9 | 14.3 | 10.5 |
| Vegetables and fruits | 4.5 | 4.8 | 4.3 | 4.5 | 4.7 | 5.0 |
| Roots and tubers | 4.0 | 2.7 | 4.0 | 2.9 | 4.0 | 2.5 |
| Other vegetable products | 1.5 | 1.5 | 1.8 | 2.1 | 1.2 | 1.2 |
| Animal products | 33.7 | 35.5 | 53.6 | 57.7 | 18.9 | 24.2 |
| Meat and offal | 15.6 | 17.2 | 24.9 | 28.3 | 8.8 | 11.6 |
| Milk | 10.4 | 9.6 | 17.4 | 16.6 | 5.2 | 6.0 |
| Fish | 5.2 | 5.9 | 7.0 | 8.6 | 3.9 | 4.5 |
| Eggs | 2.4 | 2.8 | 4.1 | 4.1 | 1.1 | 2.1 |
| Animal oils and fats | 0.1 | 0.1 | 0.1 | 0.1 | 0.0 | 0.0 |

| Food group | Developed countries | | | | Developing countries | | | | | |
|---|---|---|---|---|---|---|---|---|---|---|
| | Industrialized | | Transition economies | | Least developed | | Low-income food-deficit | | Low-income | |
| | 1969-71 | 1990-92 | 1969-71 | 1990-92 | 1969-71 | 1990-92 | 1969-71 | 1990-92 | 1969-71 | 1990-92 |
| | | | | | *(Percentage)* | | | | | |
| Vegetable products | 41.4 | 39.0 | 56.0 | 49.3 | 80.9 | 82.3 | 84.6 | 78.9 | 85.5 | 79.5 |
| Cereals | 26.4 | 24.2 | 43.4 | 39.2 | 56.4 | 60.0 | 59.2 | 59.3 | 60.1 | 60.5 |
| Pulses and nuts | 4.6 | 4.8 | 3.2 | 1.9 | 14.9 | 13.2 | 15.2 | 10.8 | 15.3 | 10.2 |
| Vegetables and fruits | 5.0 | 5.0 | 3.2 | 3.4 | 3.7 | 3.4 | 4.7 | 4.9 | 4.6 | 5.0 |
| Roots and tubers | 3.2 | 2.6 | 5.4 | 3.6 | 4.1 | 4.3 | 4.4 | 2.7 | 4.4 | 2.7 |
| Other veg. products | 2.3 | 2.5 | 0.8 | 1.1 | 1.7 | 1.3 | 1.2 | 1.1 | 1.1 | 1.1 |
| Animal products | 58.6 | 61.0 | 44.0 | 50.7 | 19.1 | 17.7 | 15.4 | 21.1 | 14.5 | 20.5 |
| Meat and offal | 28.4 | 30.5 | 18.2 | 23.5 | 9.2 | 8.3 | 6.8 | 9.9 | 6.6 | 9.8 |
| Milk | 17.6 | 17.5 | 17.0 | 14.7 | 4.8 | 5.0 | 4.2 | 5.1 | 4.0 | 5.1 |
| Fish | 7.6 | 8.8 | 5.9 | 8.2 | 4.5 | 3.9 | 3.5 | 4.1 | 3.2 | 3.6 |
| Eggs | 4.8 | 4.0 | 2.8 | 4.1 | 0.5 | 0.5 | 0.8 | 1.9 | 0.8 | 1.9 |
| Animal oils and fats | 0.1 | 0.1 | 0.1 | 0.1 | 0.0 | 0.0 | 0.0 | 0.0 | 0.0 | 0.0 |

*(continued)*

*(continued)*

**TABLE 8**

| SHARE OF MAJOR FOOD GROUPS IN TOTAL PROTEIN SUPPLIES BY REGION AND ECONOMIC GROUP, 1969-71 AND 1990-92 | | | | | | | | | |
|---|---|---|---|---|---|---|---|---|---|
| **Food group** | **Developing regions** | | | | | | | | |
| | Latin America and Caribbean | | Sub-Saharan Africa | | Near East and North Africa | | East and Southeast Asia | | South Asia | |
| | 1969-71 | 1990-92 | 1969-71 | 1990-92 | 1969-71 | 1990-92 | 1969-71 | 1990-92 | 1969-71 | 1990-92 |
| | *(Percentage)* | | | | | | | | | |
| **Vegetable products** | 61.9 | 57.1 | 79.6 | 79.2 | 78.7 | 77.4 | 84.5 | 75.8 | 86.7 | 82.6 |
| Cereals | 37.6 | 38.1 | 45.7 | 48.2 | 63.6 | 60.8 | 60.6 | 59.1 | 63.1 | 62.3 |
| Pulses and nuts | 14.6 | 10.8 | 19.0 | 16.8 | 7.1 | 7.6 | 12.9 | 8.2 | 17.1 | 13.2 |
| Vegetables and fruits | 4.1 | 3.9 | 4.6 | 4.4 | 6.0 | 6.4 | 5.1 | 5.5 | 3.9 | 4.3 |
| Roots and tubers | 3.8 | 2.6 | 8.3 | 7.9 | 1.0 | 1.6 | 5.6 | 2.4 | 0.8 | 1.1 |
| Other veg. products | 1.9 | 1.7 | 2.1 | 1.9 | 1.1 | 1.2 | 0.4 | 0.6 | 1.9 | 1.7 |
| **Animal products** | 38.1 | 42.9 | 20.4 | 20.8 | 21.3 | 22.6 | 15.5 | 24.2 | 13.3 | 17.4 |
| Meat and offal | 21.8 | 24.2 | 10.7 | 10.4 | 8.9 | 10.0 | 7.5 | 13.2 | 3.4 | 4.0 |
| Milk | 11.4 | 12.2 | 4.8 | 5.2 | 10.2 | 8.9 | 0.8 | 1.3 | 7.4 | 10.4 |
| Fish | 2.9 | 3.3 | 4.3 | 4.4 | 1.3 | 1.9 | 5.7 | 6.6 | 2.1 | 2.3 |
| Eggs | 1.9 | 3.1 | 0.6 | 0.8 | 0.8 | 1.7 | 1.5 | 3.1 | 0.3 | 0.7 |
| Animal oils and fats | 0.1 | 0.1 | 0.0 | 0.0 | 0.1 | 0.1 | 0.0 | 0.0 | 0.0 | 0.0 |

27

1969-71 to 24 percent in 1990-92, whereas in the developing countries as a whole the share rose from about 19 to 24 percent.

The situation regarding the sources of fat supply is different again (Table 9). The share of animal products in total fat supplies has been falling both in developed countries and in the world as a whole but rising in the developing countries. While the share of animal products declined from nearly 64 to 58 percent in the developed countries, it increased slightly from 36 to 38 percent in the developing countries. However, this increase was confined almost entirely to East and Southeast Asia and, to a lesser extent, to South Asia; elsewhere in the developing world the share of animal products in total fat supplies actually declined over the two decades from 1969-71.

These changes suggest that some regions are diversifying their diets more than others. The nature and extent of such diversification can be gauged from Table 10 which shows the share in total energy supplies of

**TABLE 9**

## SHARE OF MAJOR FOOD GROUPS IN TOTAL FAT SUPPLIES BY REGION AND ECONOMIC GROUP, 1969-71 AND 1990-92

| Food group | World | | Developed countries | | Developing countries | |
|---|---|---|---|---|---|---|
| | 1969-71 | 1990-92 | 1969-71 | 1990-92 | 1969-71 | 1990-92 |
| *(Percentage)* | | | | | | |
| **Vegetable products** | 48.0 | 53.3 | 36.3 | 41.7 | 63.7 | 62.0 |
| Vegetable oils and fats | 28.7 | 36.6 | 27.6 | 33.3 | 30.2 | 39.1 |
| Cereals | 9.7 | 8.3 | 3.8 | 3.3 | 17.7 | 12.2 |
| Pulses and nuts | 6.8 | 6.1 | 3.1 | 3.3 | 11.8 | 8.2 |
| Other vegetable products | 2.7 | 2.3 | 1.8 | 1.9 | 3.9 | 2.6 |
| **Animal products** | 52.0 | 46.7 | 63.7 | 58.3 | 36.3 | 38.0 |
| Meat and offal | 22.8 | 23.9 | 25.9 | 26.7 | 18.6 | 21.8 |
| Milk | 11.9 | 9.7 | 15.0 | 13.6 | 7.7 | 6.8 |
| Animal oils and fats | 13.4 | 9.0 | 18.0 | 13.1 | 7.2 | 6.0 |
| Eggs | 2.5 | 2.6 | 3.2 | 2.9 | 1.5 | 2.3 |
| Fish | 1.4 | 1.5 | 1.6 | 2.0 | 1.2 | 1.1 |

| Food group | Developed countries | | | | Developing countries | | | | | |
|---|---|---|---|---|---|---|---|---|---|---|
| | Industrialized | | Transition economies | | Least developed | | Low-income food-deficit | | Low-income | |
| | 1969-71 | 1990-92 | 1969-71 | 1990-92 | 1969-71 | 1990-92 | 1969-71 | 1990-92 | 1969-71 | 1990-92 |
| *(Percentage)* | | | | | | | | | | |
| **Vegetable products** | 38.4 | 45.1 | 30.7 | 32.2 | 70.8 | 74.6 | 67.5 | 62.3 | 67.0 | 60.6 |
| Vegetable oils and fats | 30.1 | 36.4 | 20.9 | 24.1 | 29.5 | 38.1 | 29.8 | 36.9 | 29.3 | 35.6 |
| Cereals | 2.9 | 2.7 | 6.3 | 5.0 | 22.2 | 21.3 | 20.2 | 13.6 | 21.0 | 14.2 |
| Pulses and nuts | 3.5 | 3.9 | 1.8 | 1.5 | 15.1 | 11.7 | 13.2 | 9.2 | 12.4 | 8.1 |
| Other veg. products | 1.9 | 2.1 | 1.7 | 1.5 | 4.0 | 3.5 | 4.3 | 2.7 | 4.3 | 2.7 |
| **Animal products** | 61.6 | 54.9 | 69.3 | 67.8 | 29.2 | 25.4 | 32.5 | 37.7 | 33.0 | 39.4 |
| Meat and offal | 26.9 | 26.8 | 23.0 | 26.7 | 13.1 | 11.3 | 16.8 | 22.4 | 17.4 | 23.8 |
| Milk | 13.1 | 12.8 | 20.2 | 15.7 | 8.7 | 8.2 | 6.8 | 6.3 | 6.9 | 6.5 |
| Animal oils and fats | 16.6 | 10.9 | 21.9 | 19.3 | 5.0 | 3.8 | 6.4 | 5.7 | 6.4 | 5.9 |
| Eggs | 3.4 | 2.7 | 2.8 | 3.6 | 0.8 | 0.8 | 1.3 | 2.3 | 1.3 | 2.3 |
| Fish | 1.6 | 1.8 | 1.5 | 2.5 | 1.6 | 1.3 | 1.1 | 1.0 | 1.0 | 0.9 |

*(continued)*

(continued)

**TABLE 9**

| Food group | Developing regions | | | | | | | | | |
|---|---|---|---|---|---|---|---|---|---|---|
| | Latin America and Caribbean | | Sub-Saharan Africa | | Near East and North Africa | | East and Southeast Asia | | South Asia | |
| | 1969-71 | 1990-92 | 1969-71 | 1990-92 | 1969-71 | 1990-92 | 1969-71 | 1990-92 | 1969-71 | 1990-92 |
| | | | | | *(Percentage)* | | | | | |
| **Vegetable products** | 48.2 | 56.5 | 78.0 | 78.7 | 64.0 | 71.5 | 59.6 | 52.2 | 73.6 | 72.2 |
| Vegetable oils and fats | 29.8 | 44.0 | 37.4 | 45.1 | 39.4 | 50.6 | 22.2 | 30.4 | 34.2 | 43.4 |
| Cereals | 9.2 | 7.1 | 19.0 | 17.0 | 15.6 | 12.3 | 19.1 | 11.0 | 22.5 | 15.9 |
| Pulses and nuts | 6.4 | 3.4 | 17.2 | 12.6 | 6.3 | 6.0 | 13.3 | 8.4 | 13.6 | 10.2 |
| Other veg. products | 2.8 | 2.0 | 4.4 | 4.0 | 2.7 | 2.6 | 5.1 | 2.4 | 3.3 | 2.6 |
| **Animal products** | 51.8 | 43.5 | 22.0 | 21.3 | 36.0 | 28.5 | 40.4 | 47.8 | 26.4 | 27.8 |
| Meat and offal | 27.1 | 22.6 | 10.5 | 9.9 | 11.5 | 10.2 | 29.1 | 36.8 | 4.5 | 4.0 |
| Milk | 11.8 | 10.0 | 6.4 | 6.5 | 12.3 | 8.8 | 1.4 | 1.4 | 12.4 | 13.7 |
| Animal oils and fats | 10.3 | 7.9 | 3.5 | 2.9 | 10.9 | 7.2 | 5.2 | 4.3 | 8.3 | 8.6 |
| Eggs | 1.8 | 2.3 | 0.6 | 0.7 | 1.0 | 1.8 | 2.7 | 3.6 | 0.4 | 0.9 |
| Fish | 0.7 | 0.7 | 1.1 | 1.2 | 0.4 | 0.6 | 2.0 | 1.7 | 0.8 | 0.6 |

**SHARE OF MAJOR FOOD GROUPS IN TOTAL FAT SUPPLIES BY REGION AND ECONOMIC GROUP, 1969-71 AND 1990-92**

29

whatever happens to be the major food group in a country. The lower the share, the more diversified a country's diet is assumed to be. Using this criterion, it is obvious that the diets of the developed world are much more diversified than those of the developing world but there are two interesting points to note. First, even in the developed regions there are countries (such as South Africa and Albania) in which the extent of diversification is no greater than the average of the developing world while, on the other hand, the diversification level achieved in Latin America is close to that of the transition economies. Second, in all developing regions except sub-Saharan Africa, the extent of diversification is increasing over time, especially in the countries of the two groups, East and Southeast Asia and the Near East and North Africa.

Another aspect of food composition pertains to the relative importance of major staple cereals and roots in the world. As can be seen from Table 11, rice continues to be the major cereal in the world, followed closely by wheat. The share of rice actually increased somewhat between 1969-71

TABLE 10

## EXTENT OF DIVERSIFICATION OF NATIONAL DIETS BY REGION, 1969-71 AND 1990-92

| Region/economic group | Share of the main food group[1] in DES | | |
|---|---|---|---|
| | Average of countries in region | Most diversified country | Least diversified country |
| | *(Percentage)* | | |
| **Industrialized countries** | | | |
| 1969-71 | 27.9 | 18.8 (United States) | 52.8 (South Africa) |
| 1990-92 | 25.8 | 16.9 (Netherlands) | 53.7 (South Africa) |
| **Transition economies** | | | |
| 1969-71 | 46.1 | 32.5 (Czechoslovakia) | 63.9 (Albania) |
| 1990-92 | 40.8 | 28.8 (Hungary) | 61.6 (Albania) |
| **Latin America and the Caribbean** | | | |
| 1969-71 | 41.3 | 25.1 (Dominican Rep.) | 63.0 (Guatemala) |
| 1990-92 | 40.5 | 24.0 (Paraguay) | 60.0 (Guatemala) |
| **Sub-Saharan Africa** | | | |
| 1969-71 | 50.8 | 23.8 (Uganda) | 81.4 (Lesotho) |
| 1990-92 | 50.2 | 25.9 (Gabon) | 77.8 (Lesotho) |
| **Near East and North Africa** | | | |
| 1969-71 | 58.4 | 43.4 (Kuwait) | 80.5 (Afghanistan) |
| 1990-92 | 53.1 | 33.7 (United Arab Emirates) | 76.3 (Afghanistan) |
| **East and Southeast Asia** | | | |
| 1969-71 | 66.6 | 45.7 (Mongolia) | 84.1 (Cambodia) |
| 1990-92 | 60.7 | 33.5 (Hong Kong) | 84.7 (Cambodia) |
| **South Asia** | | | |
| 1969-71 | 69.4 | 55.5 (Sri Lanka) | 81.0 (Nepal) |
| 1990-92 | 67.7 | 55.8 (Pakistan) | 83.8 (Bangladesh) |

[1] The main food group is that with the highest share in a country's total DES.

and 1990-92, but this was mainly because the population share of the rice-eating parts of the world increased during this time. In the major rice-eating areas, i.e. East, Southeast and South Asia, the share of rice in total energy supplies actually declined over the two decades while that of wheat increased. The share of maize in the total world DES increased from 5.4 to 6.1 percent between 1969-71 and 1990-92. The increase in the percentage was significant in the industrialized countries and in sub-Saharan Africa. However, there was a decline in the Near East and North Africa as well as in South Asia. In Latin America and the Caribbean,

**TABLE 11**

## SHARE OF MAIN CEREALS AND ROOTS IN TOTAL DES BY REGION, 1969-71 AND 1990-92

| Region/economic group | Share in total DES | | | | |
| --- | --- | --- | --- | --- | --- |
| | Rice | Wheat | Maize | Sorghum and millet | Cassava |
| | *(Percentage)* | | | | |
| **World** | | | | | |
| 1969-71 | 20.3 | 17.5 | 5.4 | 4.4 | 1.7 |
| 1990-92 | 22.0 | 19.5 | 6.1 | 2.6 | 1.6 |
| **Industrialized countries** | | | | | |
| 1969-71 | 5.1 | 18.5 | 2.0 | 0.1 | 0.0 |
| 1990-92 | 4.4 | 17.3 | 3.2 | 0.1 | 0.0 |
| **Transition economies** | | | | | |
| 1969-71 | 1.1 | 32.7 | 1.4 | 0.6 | 0.0 |
| 1990-92 | 1.3 | 32.9 | 1.2 | 0.2 | 0.0 |
| **Latin America and the Caribbean** | | | | | |
| 1969-71 | 9.0 | 13.9 | 15.7 | 0.3 | 4.2 |
| 1990-92 | 9.4 | 13.2 | 15.3 | 0.1 | 2.2 |
| **Sub-Saharan Africa** | | | | | |
| 1969-71 | 4.8 | 3.6 | 13.5 | 19.2 | 14.3 |
| 1990-92 | 7.8 | 5.4 | 14.7 | 14.6 | 14.9 |
| **Near East and North Africa** | | | | | |
| 1969-71 | 6.2 | 41.7 | 6.1 | 2.6 | 0.0 |
| 1990-92 | 6.2 | 42.8 | 4.7 | 0.8 | 0.0 |
| **East and Southeast Asia** | | | | | |
| 1969-71 | 43.9 | 9.8 | 6.8 | 4.6 | 1.1 |
| 1990-92 | 40.8 | 17.1 | 6.8 | 0.9 | 0.9 |
| **South Asia** | | | | | |
| 1969-71 | 35.4 | 16.8 | 3.4 | 10.5 | 0.0 |
| 1990-92 | 33.7 | 21.0 | 2.8 | 6.6 | 0.5 |

where maize is the most significant staple food, its share in the DES remained essentially unchanged, as it also did in the transition economies and in East and Southeast Asia. Among the minor cereals, the share of sorghum and millet declined at the world level, mainly because of their declining importance in the populous parts of Asia; cassava, on the other hand, maintained its standing in sub-Saharan Africa, although it is losing its already reduced importance in Latin America.

# CHAPTER 2

# Prevalence and intensity of food inadequacy in developing countries

•

Methodological issues

•

Reliability of data and models

•

Results: magnitude and trends of food inadequacy in developing countries

•

Intensity of food inadequacy

This chapter explores the implications that the levels and changes in per caput DES presented in Chapter 1 have for the extent of food inadequacy in the developing regions. To do so, it is necessary to look beyond the overall per caput food availability (which merely shows how the average person has fared in each country) and take into account the distribution of food within a population.

Based on the distribution of food intake, two measures of food inadequacy are presented which are analogous to the well-known head count and income gap measures of poverty. The first is called the *prevalence* of food inadequacy and shows the proportion and number of people in a given population whose food access is deemed to be inadequate; the second is called the *intensity* of food inadequacy, and it shows the amount of additional food that is needed to eliminate the prevalence of food inadequacy.

## METHODOLOGICAL ISSUES

An accurate assessment of the number of people and proportion of a population with inadequate access to food requires data from national sample surveys designed to measure both the food consumption and the food requirements of individuals, i.e. specialized food consumption or dietary intake surveys. Unfortunately, however, national surveys of this kind are costly and time-consuming to implement and have been undertaken in very few countries. Therefore, to generate a distribution curve of access to food (expressed in dietary energy terms) for each country, FAO has developed a methodology that uses the per caput DES data from food balance sheets combined with an estimate of variations in food consumption derived from a variety of sources. By applying a cutoff point based on the concept of minimum energy requirements, the prevalence of food inadequacy is estimated.

The methodological framework for the present estimates is essentially the same as that adopted in *The Fifth World Food Survey*, although a number of improvements have been made. Appendix 3 provides a detailed and comprehensive account of this methodology, of which a brief account is given here.

### Basic steps of the methodology

i) It is assumed that the pattern of the distribution of per caput dietary energy (calorie) consumption within each country is log-normal so that the levels of energy consumption throughout a population can be calculated simply from the mean and the standard deviation (SD) (see Appendix 3 for details). Thus, based on the per caput DES derived from the FAO food balance sheets and on an estimated value of the coefficient of variation (CV), the distribution of per caput calorie consumption is generated for each country. The CV is kept constant throughout the three periods under study (1969-71, 1979-81 and 1990-92), so the extent of inequality in the distribution is assumed to have remained unchanged. This admittedly unsatisfactory assumption is necessary because, for most of the countries under study, little is known about any change in distribution that might have occurred during the last two decades.

ii) Based on nutritional considerations, an estimate is made of the minimum per caput dietary energy requirement (cutoff point) below which the average person's intake is considered to be inadequate – the average person being defined as the weighted average of one person from each of the age-sex groups adopted for estimating energy requirements.

iii) The next step is to calculate the proportion of the population that consumes less than the minimum requirement, using the distribution of per caput calorie consumption (obtained following step i above) and the minimum per caput energy requirement.

iv) Finally, the calculated proportion is multiplied by the size of the total population to obtain an estimate of the number of people who have inadequate access to food.

### Details of specification and departures from *The Fifth World Food Survey*

It is clear from this basic account of the methodology that, given the per caput DES and population figures for a country, the prevalence estimates would be determined by the consumption distribution variability parameter, i.e. the CV, and the minimum per caput dietary energy requirement. The specification of both presents considerable problems owing to a lack of appropriate data as well as conceptual difficulties. These problems are discussed in depth in Appendix 3 but some of the salient points are mentioned below. In the light of new knowledge gained since *The Fifth World Food Survey*, a number of methodological improvements have been introduced; it should be emphasized that all were retroactively applied to the three periods under consideration in order to generate comparable results that warrant an analysis over time. These changes are indicated at the appropriate points and are also discussed in detail in Appendix 3.

*The coefficient of variation.* Wherever possible, this parameter, which refers to the ratio of the SD to the mean, is derived from the sample distribution of per caput calorie consumption as measured in national household surveys. These surveys are corrected to remove the component of variation resulting from short-term (weekly, monthly or seasonal) fluctuations in consumption so as to allow a final estimate of variation in "habitual" dietary energy consumption that is consistent with the annual per caput average value based on food balance sheets. For countries where such direct estimates of variation are not available, recourse has to be made either to estimates derived from household income or expenditure surveys or, in the "worst cases" where no distributional data of any kind are available, to the use of the average CV for other countries in the same region.

The analysis of interhousehold variations in per caput calorie consumption has also led to the definition of a plausible range for the CV. The lower and upper limits of this range have been set at 0.20 and 0.35, respectively. Hence, if a CV calculated for a country (after adjustment) was found to be outside this range, it was replaced by either 0.20 or 0.35, depending on whether the figure was below the lower limit or above the upper limit. This is a departure from *The Fifth World Food Survey* approach in which no a priori limit was imposed on the CV value.

*Minimum per caput dietary energy requirement.* The concept of a minimum dietary energy requirement is explained at length in Appendix 3 so only a brief definition is given here: an individual can be considered to have a more or less fixed energy requirement whereas a group of people of the same age-sex type will have a range of requirements; and people whose intake falls within this range will tend to adjust it to meet their respective requirements (FAO/WHO/UNU, 1985). If such people were completely free to adjust their intake, then obviously none would suffer from food inadequacy. However, in reality there may not be such freedom of choice, so food inadequacy may still exist among certain people. But it is safe to assume that, if the intakes of a group of people are high enough to fall within the range of requirements, the constraints on their food access, if any, cannot be too severe and most of them are likely to have an intake that is fairly close to their requirements. This argument implies that a group of people whose intake falls within the range of requirements can be considered to be at a low or "acceptable" risk of food inadequacy. By implication, people whose intake falls below the range of requirements can be said to be at a high or "unacceptable" risk of food inadequacy. It is the latter group that the present methodology seeks to identify. In other words, the term "prevalence of food inadequacy" refers to those people who face a high risk of food inadequacy in the above sense. Accordingly, with the exception of children below the age of ten, the minimum energy requirement for individuals of an age-sex type is defined as the lower end of the range of requirements for that type. This is also called the cutoff point for the simple reason that this point is used to set apart people who are at an unacceptable risk of food inadequacy from the rest. The aggregate minimum energy requirement, or the overall cutoff point, to be applied to the aggregated per caput intake distribution is derived as a weighted average of the age-sex specific minimum requirements.[5]

For estimating the energy requirements of different age-sex groups, the basic methodology recommended by the FAO/WHO/UNU Expert Consultation on Energy and Protein Requirements (FAO/WHO/UNU, 1985) has been followed. This methodology derives energy requirements by adding up components of energy expenditure: for each component, the level of energy expenditure that is consistent with good health and an active life is assumed. The main components are the basal metabolic rate (BMR) which essentially refers to the amount of energy needed to keep the body in a satisfactory condition while at rest, and the energy required for physical activity. In addition to these components, an allowance is made for additional energy demands occasioned by pregnancy and lactation among women and physical growth in children.

Within this overall framework, the practical procedure of estimating energy requirements differs slightly, as it does between children and adults. In both cases, the first step is to specify a set of reference body weights for each age-sex group. The difference is in the next step: for children up to the age of ten, energy requirements are obtained directly by applying to the reference body weight the set of energy requirements per kilogram of body weight given in FAO/WHO/UNU (1985); for adults and adolescents, first the age-sex specific BMR is estimated, using the appropriate equations linking BMR with weight, and then an allowance is added for physical activity, expressed as a multiple of the BMR.

It is clear from the preceding account that estimates of energy requirements depend crucially on the body weights and activity levels specified for different age-sex groups. A few comments are therefore in order regarding their specification as used in this report. Since the cutoff point has (in the case of adults and adolescents) been defined as the lower end of the range of requirements, it follows that, as determinants of requirements, body weight and activity levels should also be chosen at the *minimum* levels that are consistent with the good health and functioning of the specific age-sex groups. Accordingly, requirement estimates have been based on the lower end of the variation in body weights and physical activity that is generally observed among healthy people of the same group. The same principle was followed in *The Fifth World Food Survey*, but with some important differences.

---

[5] The weighting is according to the proportion of the population in the different age-sex groups.

In the previous survey, the minimum acceptable body weight for adults and adolescents was obtained by using data provided, respectively, by the New York Society of Actuaries and the Baldwin tables. The former gave a range of normal weights for height for different age-sex groups, and the minimum value of this range was applied to actual heights of age-sex groups in developing countries to obtain the minimum acceptable body weight. New data are used in the present survey because the old figures were based on mortality rates obtained many years ago in a selected United States population and because a considerable number of data on the weights and heights of people in developing countries have now become available. One particular measure of weight-height relationship that has been found to be a good indicator of health and nutrition in adults is the body mass index (BMI), defined as weight (in kilograms) divided by height (in metres) squared (see Appendix 4). It has also been found that there is a range of BMI which is consistent with good health, and the lower end of this range has been identified as 18.5 for both men and women (Shetty and James in FAO, 1994b). Accordingly, for the present assessment the minimum acceptable body weight for adults and adolescents has been calculated by applying the BMI value of 18.5 to the average height of different age-sex groups in different countries.

As regards adding an allowance for physical activity, *The Fifth World Food Survey* applied the multiplier 1.4 to the BMR as a provisional figure. Today, more definitive information is available (James and Schofield, 1990); it would now appear that the multipliers 1.55 and 1.56 are more appropriate for men and women, respectively, to allow for light activity, and these new multipliers are used in the present survey.

After calculating the energy requirements of different age-sex groups on the basis of minimum body weight and activity levels, *The Fifth World Food Survey* also allowed for the possibility of an individual's energy requirements being further reduced by an adaptive increase in the efficiency of energy utilization (intra-individual variation in requirements). This possibility was based on the hypothesis that, in response to low intakes, people could adapt up to a point by reducing their energy requirements through an automatic increase in the metabolic efficiency with which their body utilizes dietary energy. However, recent research has led to a growing consensus that, for a person with a given body weight and level of activity, the range of any possible variation in the metabolic efficiency of energy utilization is very small. Accordingly, no such allowance has been made in the present survey.

As stated earlier, with regard to children below the age of ten the procedure for arriving at the cutoff point differs from that adopted for adults and adolescents. *The Fifth World Food Survey* adopted the lower limit of the range of normal body weight, as it did for adults and adolescents, but this procedure is now regarded as being unduly conservative and likely to result in a serious underestimation of the prevalence of food inadequacy among children. Therefore, in the current assessment the minimum has been replaced by the median value (see Appendix 3). On the other hand, the 5 percent allowance for additional desirable activity that was incorporated in the previous survey has been removed, while an allowance for the energy needed to recover from frequent rounds of infection is now included for children below the age of two.

It should also be noted that, in *The Fifth World Food Survey*, the population age-sex distribution that was used as a weight to aggregate the age-sex specific requirements and express them with regard to the average person (on a per caput basis) was assumed to be unchanged for each country between assessment periods. In the present assessment, the changes in age-sex distribution between the periods are taken into account.

Finally, in terms of geographical coverage, the present study goes beyond the previous survey by including estimates for the group of countries formerly classified as the Asian centrally planned economies for all three periods. As a result, the absolute number of people with inadequate access to food in the developing world turns out to be higher in this survey than in the preceding one.

## RELIABILITY OF DATA AND MODELS

As indicated in the preceding methodological discussion and Appendix 3, the estimation of the prevalence of food inadequacy is based on two key elements: the distribution of dietary energy consumption or intake within a country and the cutoff point below which the intake of the average person is considered to be inadequate. The distribution of dietary energy consumption is derived by using the log-normal frequency distribution model and estimates of the per caput DES (obtained from FAO's food balance sheets) and the CV (which in many cases is estimated indirectly through the use of regression models). The cutoff point, on the other hand, is derived for each country on the basis of estimates of the average height of individuals by age-sex group. This in turn enables the derivation of the associated minimum (median in the case of children) of the acceptable range of body weight and the application of the energy requirement norms given in FAO/WHO/UNU (1985).

It is thus evident that the reliability of the resulting estimates of the prevalence of food inadequacy depends on the accuracy of all the above-mentioned estimates and models. This section discusses this issue in a very general manner and then attempts a sensitivity analysis to identify the most important determining factor for the food inadequacy level.

Of the two key estimation elements, the cutoff point is indeed a major factor because, given the distribution of intake, it has a direct effect on the proportion of the population estimated to be underfed or undernourished. However, the fixing of this element largely concerns matters relating to nutritional norms rather than food consumption data availability or reliability (see Appendix 3) and, consequently, the focus here is on the data and models used to derive the distribution of energy intakes only.

### Data and models underlying the distribution of energy intakes

The derivation of the distribution of energy intakes involves the application of the two-parameter log-normal model as well as the use of estimates of the per caput DES and the CV of per caput energy intake to derive the two parameters (i.e. the mean and the SD). The caveats with respect to these parameters are discussed below:

*The log-normal model.* The log-normal model has been used because, in the few cases where it has been possible to obtain survey data on intake distribution, it has been found to give the best representation of empirical evidence (see Appendix 3). However, since the two-parameter log-normal distribution has no specific limits, the concern is that it is likely to result in a significant proportion of the population being assigned un-realistically low intakes and will thus overestimate the prevalence of in-adequate intakes.

To address this issue, some indication of what could be considered "unrealistically low" is needed. The few available country data on the distribution of household per caput intake show that up to 2 percent of households may have an intake of less than 750 kcal per caput/day (with the intake averaged over different age-sex groups). Therefore, for practical purposes the figure of 800 kcal per caput/day may be taken as a rough indication of what is "unrealistically low".

The risk of a significant portion of the derived distribution being below this 800 kcal level can be expected only when a very low national per caput DES (representing the mean of the distribution) is combined with the highest CV value. As mentioned in the methodological discussion, the highest CV level applied is 0.35. Thus, the issue can be addressed by examining the proportion of the population with an intake below 800 kcal per caput/day resulting from combinations of the CV of 0.35 with very low per caput DES levels. The calculated proportion of the population below 800 kcal per caput/day at alternative low per caput DES levels is given in Table 12.

Thus, in the extreme situations characterized by a very low per caput DES, when the CV is set at the maximum level of 0.35, the percentage of the population with unrealistically low intake levels is very low. Since the percentage of undernourished is more than 50 percent at such low per caput DES levels (see Table 13), the extent of overestimation is likely to be very small. The number of countries with a per caput DES of less than 1 700 kcal per caput/day is also very small. It may therefore be concluded that the absence of a lower-limit truncation in the log-normal distribution is not a matter of serious concern in the present context.

However, as the log-normal distribution is not fitted to actual data in the classical way, there is a risk that the pattern of the actual distribution may differ significantly. Therefore, its general application in all countries introduces an element of uncertainty or error in the shape of the distribution curve.

*The per caput DES.* This measure, which is taken as the mean of the intake distribution, is derived as a ratio of the total food supply to the population size. The total food supply includes food losses or wastage at the retail or household level so, at least conceptually, the per caput DES is likely to overstate the true mean energy intake level. However, the extent of overestimation is likely to be relatively small in most developing countries, where average intake levels are not high.[6] In the few countries where the per caput DES is close to or above 3 000 kcal per caput/day, the extent of overestimation can be significant. Nevertheless, even in this context the extent of exaggeration is likely to be greater in the upper rather than the lower tail of the derived distribution of intakes.

The per caput DES is derived by FAO through the food balance sheet approach. The numerator, i.e. the total food supply, is based on information relating to food production, food products traded, wastage from the farm up to the retail level, stock changes and non-food uses of food products. While data on production and trade are available for most countries, it is well known that they are often subject to errors and that there are many gaps in the information reported by countries. As regards the information on stocks and non-food utilization, comprehensive and regular statistics are not normally available and there is therefore a need to rely on estimates based on fragmentary data or assumptions.

The population estimates used as the denominator of the ratio are based on the global series prepared and updated biannually by the UN Population Division. The basic data underlying these assessments are from the national population censuses and surveys. Although most of the developing countries have carried out censuses, these invariably suffer from errors of under- or overestimation. The UN Population Division

40

---

[6] See the section Statistical database, p. 128, Appendix 3.

undertakes a significant amount of evaluation and adjustment of the basic data in deriving the series of estimates. However, the revisions of estimates for the past periods, carried out by the UN as the series are updated, together with the differences that one notes when the estimates are compared with those reported by countries or other agencies, indicate that they are not necessarily accurate. Further, these global assessments often have to rely on data that reflect the *de jure* rather than the *de facto* situation.

**TABLE 12**

**PERCENTAGE OF POPULATION WITH ENERGY INTAKE BELOW 800 KCAL PER CAPUT/DAY**

| Per caput DES | Population below 800 kcal per caput/day |
|---|---|
| (kcal/day) | (Percentage) |
| 1 600 | 3.1 |
| 1 700 | 2.0 |
| 1 800 | 1.3 |

It is therefore evident that the per caput DES estimates resulting from the ratio of total food supply to population are likely to be subject to certain margins of error, particularly where data problems are severe, for example in Africa. Although FAO undertakes consistency checks within the supply utilization framework before arriving at the per caput DES figure, this ensures that the results are within a certain plausible range and does not necessarily guarantee that they reflect the true levels.

*The CV of per caput dietary energy intakes.* The CV reflects the inequality in the distribution of dietary energy availability or supply. The advantage of using the CV rather than the SD as the measure of inequality lies in the fact that it is not correlated with the mean. This means that it can be estimated independently of the per caput DES.

However, the appropriate data sets for estimating the CV for individuals are not available. The data available at best refer to the distribution of household per caput intakes which provide an approximation of the required measure. Even in this context, the relevant survey data are available for only 18 countries (although these include large countries such as China, India, Brazil, Pakistan and Bangladesh). In view of this, for many countries, it has been necessary to base the estimates on data referring to the distribution of household per caput income or expenditure. The estimation of the CV in these cases entails the use of regression equations, linking variables chosen according to data availability rather than economically meaningful criteria. As a result, their predictive capacity is poor, particularly outside the range of values of the variables used for deriving the equations. For another group of countries, not even income or expenditure distribution data are available, so the CV had to be imputed on the basis of the CV estimated for neighbouring countries with a similar socio-economic situation.

41

The problem of adopting an unrealistically high or low CV owing to the use of the regression equations has been avoided by keeping the CVs within the acceptable range of 0.20 and 0.35. However, this cannot ensure that the CVs adopted reflect the true levels in the different countries, particularly since the same CV has been applied to all the three periods under study.

The above remarks suggest that an analytically derived intake distribution runs the risk of inadequately reflecting the true distribution, thereby leading to errors of an unknown magnitude and direction in the estimate of the prevalence of food inadequacy for a given country. Needless to say, the greater the extent to which the available data have been extended by assumptions or models to arrive at the required parameters, the greater the likelihood of errors. In some countries the risk of error is likely to be particularly high, for example in Ethiopia, PDR, Somalia, Rwanda and Afghanistan, where civil strife has disrupted not only the normal food availability and distribution system but also the data collection system. These countries generally have a large refugee population living outside their borders, in which case serious problems are faced in arriving at plausible estimates of the total food supply and the size of the population partaking of it (and hence the per caput DES). Therefore, the very low per caput DES levels estimated for these countries need to be interpreted with extreme caution.

### Sensitivity of prevalence of food inadequacy estimates to per caput DES and CV

On the assumption that the general application of the log-normal distribution is plausible and that the cutoff point can be taken as a given parameter, the proportion of the population with inadequate access to food is determined by the per caput DES and the CV. Therefore, as there

TABLE 13

**PREVALANCE OF FOOD INADEQUACY AT DIFFERENT LEVELS OF PER CAPUT DES AND CV**

| Per caput DES | CV | | | |
|---|---|---|---|---|
| | 0.20 | 0.24 | 0.29 | 0.35 |
| (kcal/day) | | (Percentage of undernourished) | | |
| 1 700[1] | 65 | 64 | 63 | 63 |
| 2 040 | 30 | 34 | 38 | 42 |
| 2 450 | 7 | 12 | 17 | 23 |
| 2 940 | 1 | 2 | 6 | 10 |

[1] It should be noted that, at such low average levels, the percentage of undernourished rises rather than falls with a decline in the CV. This is because the implied aggregate food supply is so low that to achieve less inequality would mean increasing the proportion below the cutoff point.

is more likelihood of errors with the CV than with the per caput DES, it is useful to undertake a sensitivity analysis to assess which of the two is more important in determining the general food inadequacy level. This can be done by examining the extent of the change in the proportion of population with inadequate access to food, resulting from a proportional change in each of the two measures taken in turn.

The cutoff point is assumed to correspond to 1 800 kcal per caput/day and the per caput DES and CV are given initial values of 1 700 kcal per caput/day and 0.20, respectively. Both of these are then successively increased by 20 percent in three steps to arrive at the levels of 2 940 kcal per caput/day and 0.35. This produces 16 combinations of per caput DES and CV levels, according to which the resulting prevalence of food inadequacy is given in Table 13. The changes in the percentage of undernourished as the CV is successively increased by 20 percent are indicated in the rows moving towards the right, while the changes in the percentage of undernourished as the per caput DES is similarly increased are indicated downwards in the columns. Thus, the absolute change in percentage along the rows indicates the sensitivity to the CV at a given per caput DES level while the change down the columns indicates the sensitivity to the per caput DES at a given CV level.

It can be seen that, when the per caput DES is low and close to the cutoff point, the percentage is not only at its highest levels but it is also practically insensitive to changes in the CV. Sensitivity to the CV tends to increase gradually as the per caput DES moves above the cutoff point. In the present analysis, which assumes a cutoff point of 1 800 kcal per caput/day, it appears to reach a maximum when the per caput DES level of about 2 500 kcal per caput/day is reached. However, even at this maximum point, the absolute change in the percentage resulting from a change in the per caput DES is more than that resulting from a proportionate change in the CV. In other words, sensitivity to the per caput DES is greater than it is to the CV, even when the effect of the latter is at its maximum.

Given a cutoff point, therefore, the most important determining factor in the general level of food inadequacy is the per caput DES. This means that the expectation of greater errors in the CV compared with the per caput DES is not of great concern. Nevertheless, because of the caveats mentioned, the resulting estimates of the prevalence of food inadequacy need to be interpreted with caution, particularly at the country level. For this reason, the present survey focuses on broad levels and trends only. The basic intention is to provide indications of the broad magnitudes of the food inadequacy problem in different parts of the developing world by piecing together all the data available on food consumption at the country level, however incomplete or imprecise they may be.

43

# RESULTS: MAGNITUDE AND TRENDS OF FOOD INADEQUACY IN DEVELOPING COUNTRIES

## Interpretation of the estimates

When interpreting the estimates of food inadequacy presented below, two points should be borne in mind. First, for reasons discussed in the Introduction, the terms "inadequate food intake" and "inadequate access to food" cannot be equated with undernutrition as tends to be done in popular discussions. Even leaving aside the problem of measurement errors, for conceptual and methodological reasons alone the estimates of food inadequacy presented here must be seen as an approximation of the true extent of undernutrition. This caveat should be remembered if, by deferring to convention, the following estimates are used to refer to undernutrition. Second, as it is presented here, the prevalence of food inadequacy refers to the situation prevailing on the average over a relatively long period. This is because the estimates are based on "habitual" food intake defined as the average intake over a three-year period. Over shorter time spans (e.g. a month, a season, or even a year) the actual prevalence may well deviate from these estimates.

## Developing countries as a whole and by region

During the two decades from 1969-71, the prevalence of food inadequacy declined in the developing countries as a whole: 20 percent of their total population had inadequate access to food in 1990-92 compared with 35 percent only two decades ago (Table 14). Even more remarkably, there was also an improvement in absolute terms, i.e. fewer people had inadequate access to food in 1990-92 compared with 20 years ago, notwithstanding the population increase of about 1.5 billion in the developing countries during this time. As shown in Table 14, the number of people with inadequate access to food declined from 918 million in 1969-71 to 906 million in 1979-81 and further to 841 million in 1990-92. Nevertheless, the number was still very high in 1990-92, as one out of five people in the developing countries had inadequate access to food.

A more disaggregated analysis shows that the overall improvement for the developing countries as a whole masks very different regional trends (Figure 4). During the last decade, the proportion of the population with inadequate food either remained unchanged or increased in sub-Saharan Africa, the Near East and North Africa and Latin America and the Caribbean. Of these regions, sub-Saharan Africa had the worst experience, as the proportion of the population as well as the absolute number of people with inadequate access to food increased over both decades. The proportion increased from 38 percent in 1969-71

**TABLE 14**

**PREVALENCE OF FOOD INADEQUACY IN DEVELOPING REGIONS, 1969-71, 1979-81 AND 1990-92**

| Region/economic group | Period | Total population (Millions) | Proportion undernourished (Percentage) | Number undernourished (Millions) |
|---|---|---|---|---|
| **REGION** | | | | |
| Sub-Saharan Africa | 1969-71 | 270 | 38 | 103 |
| | 1979-81 | 359 | 41 | 148 |
| | 1990-92 | 501 | 43 | 215 |
| Near East and North Africa | 1969-71 | 180 | 27 | 48 |
| | 1979-81 | 236 | 12 | 27 |
| | 1990-92 | 323 | 12 | 37 |
| East and Southeast Asia | 1969-71 | 1 166 | 41 | 476 |
| | 1979-81 | 1 417 | 27 | 379 |
| | 1990-92 | 1 694 | 16 | 269 |
| South Asia | 1969-71 | 711 | 33 | 238 |
| | 1979-81 | 892 | 34 | 303 |
| | 1990-92 | 1 138 | 22 | 255 |
| Latin America and the Caribbean | 1969-71 | 279 | 19 | 53 |
| | 1979-81 | 354 | 14 | 48 |
| | 1990-92 | 443 | 15 | 64 |
| **ECONOMIC GROUP** | | | | |
| Low-income | 1969-71 | 1 934 | 39 | 752 |
| | 1979-81 | 2 397 | 33 | 783 |
| | 1990-92 | 3 000 | 23 | 696 |
| Middle- to high-income | 1969-71 | 674 | 25 | 166 |
| | 1979-81 | 863 | 14 | 123 |
| | 1990-92 | 1 104 | 13 | 144 |
| **Developing regions** | 1969-71 | 2 608 | 35 | 918 |
| | 1979-81 | 3 260 | 28 | 906 |
| | 1990-92 | 4 104 | 20 | 841 |

45

to 43 percent in 1990-92 and, with population growing at an annual rate of 2.9 percent, the absolute number approximately doubled from 103 million to 215 million in the same period. As a result of this worsening situation, the share of sub-Saharan Africa in the total number of people with inadequate food access in the developing world shot up from 11 percent in 1969-71 to 26 percent in 1990-92 (Figure 5). This dramatic collapse in access to food is not surprising in view of the unusual droughts experienced by many of the countries in the region during the 1980s and early 1990s. In addition, a series of wars and civil strife inevitably took their toll.

In the Near East and North Africa and in the Latin American and Caribbean countries, the proportion of people with inadequate access to food remained fairly stable but the absolute number increased, from 27 million in 1979-81 to 37 million in 1990-92 in the Near East and North Africa and from 48 million to 64 million in Latin America and the

**FIGURE 4**

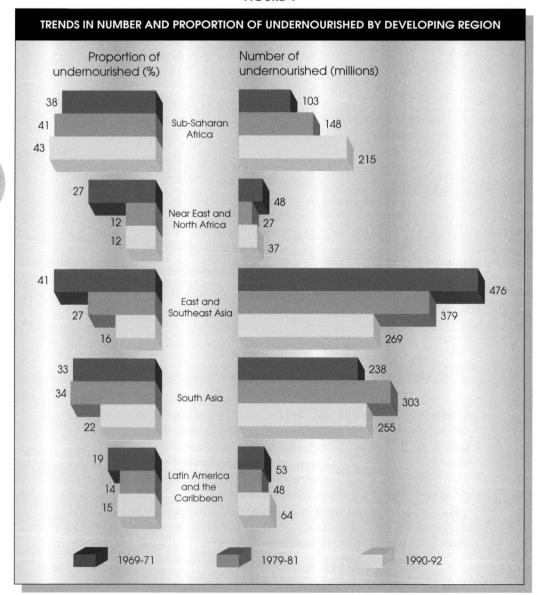

TRENDS IN NUMBER AND PROPORTION OF UNDERNOURISHED BY DEVELOPING REGION

46

Caribbean. In South Asia, the proportion remained more or less constant in the 1970s and then declined in the 1980s but, because of the region's large population and high rate of population growth, the absolute number of people with inadequate food did not decline significantly after 1969-71.

In sharp contrast with all other regions, East and Southeast Asia experienced a continued improvement over the 20-year period. The proportion of the population with inadequate access to food dropped from 41 percent in 1969-71 to 27 percent in 1979-81 and further to only 16 percent in 1990-92. Even more remarkably, despite continued population growth, the absolute number of people with inadequate access to food also declined from 476 million in 1969-71 to 269 million in 1990-92. However, because of its large population, this region still accounts for the highest share of people facing food inadequacy in the developing world, although its share has declined over time from just over half in 1969-71 to about one-third in 1990-92.

Among the economic groups of countries, the proportion of the population with inadequate food access declined for all groups but was still as high as 23 percent in low-income countries in 1990-92 compared with 13 percent in middle- to high-income countries. The low-income countries account for about 83 percent of all people with inadequate access to food in the developing countries.

47

**FIGURE 5**

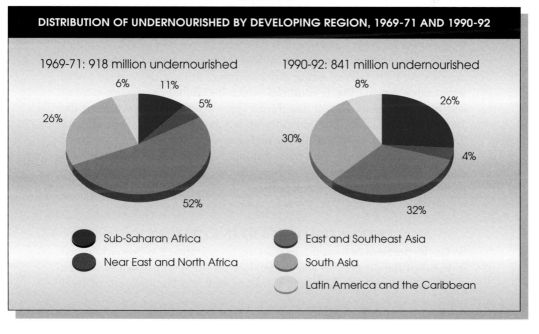

DISTRIBUTION OF UNDERNOURISHED BY DEVELOPING REGION, 1969-71 AND 1990-92

1969-71: 918 million undernourished

1990-92: 841 million undernourished

Sub-Saharan Africa

East and Southeast Asia

Near East and North Africa

South Asia

Latin America and the Caribbean

### An overview of country trends

While regional trends are informative, it is necessary to disaggregate further since substantial differences often exist even among countries within the same region. An overview of country-level experience is presented in Table 15, in which the countries are classified by three different criteria: there is the usual division between low-income and middle- to high-income countries and, within each of these two broad groups, countries are then classified according to the prevalence of food inadequacy (as measured by the proportion of undernourished population) in 1969-71. Countries in each inadequacy group are then classified according to whether the prevalence of inadequacy declined, remained stable or increased over the two decades from 1969-71 to 1990-92.

As may be seen from Table 15, among the 98 developing countries covered by the present survey, between 1969-71 and 1990-92 the prevalence of food inadequacy increased in 39 countries (28 low-income and 11 middle- to high-income countries). Thus, beneath the overall improvement in access to food in the developing world there remains the disconcerting fact that the situation actually worsened in 40 percent of the countries; in the low-income group the situation worsened in well over half the countries. Since this deterioration would be of less significance if a country had a low prevalence of food inadequacy to begin with, it is necessary to distinguish between countries with different initial levels of food inadequacy.

Considering the low-income countries first, during the two decades starting from 1969-71, the increased prevalence of food inadequacy was somewhat more evident among those countries which had a relatively low prevalence to begin with. Thus, the prevalence rates increased in two-thirds of the countries which had initial rates of less than 45 percent and in one-third of the countries which had rates above 45 percent. A similar tendency is observed among the middle- to high-income countries, with an increased prevalence being more common among those with lower initial rates. Among the 32 countries which had initial prevalence rates of less than 30 percent, almost one-third experienced increases while, of the 18 countries which had initial rates above 45 percent, only one did so. Thus, in both low- and middle- to high-income countries, the prevalence of food inadequacy increased more among countries with low initial rates and declined more among countries with higher initial rates, indicating some convergence among the countries.

## INTENSITY OF FOOD INADEQUACY

So far the problem of food inadequacy in a population has been discussed in terms of the proportion and number of people with inadequate access to food. These numbers do not, however, indicate the intensity of food

**TABLE 15**

| LEVEL AND APPARENT TREND IN PREVALENCE OF FOOD INADEQUACY[1] IN 98 DEVELOPING COUNTRIES, 1969-71 TO 1990-92 | | | |
|---|---|---|---|
| Prevalence of food inadequacy in 1969-71 | Trend in prevalence of food inadequacy, 1969-71 to 1990-92 | | |
| (Percentage) | Declined | Stable | Increased |
| **Low-income countries (48)** | | | |
| Less than 15 (1) | – | – | (1)<br>Cambodia |
| 15-30 (16) | (5)<br>Côte d'Ivoire<br>Egypt<br>Honduras<br>Laos<br>Pakistan | – | (11)<br>Bangladesh<br>Central African Rep.<br>Guyana<br>Madagascar<br>Malawi<br>Mongolia<br>Nicaragua<br>Nigeria<br>Sri Lanka<br>Uganda<br>Viet Nam |
| 30-45 (20) | (7)<br>Benin<br>Gambia<br>Guinea<br>India<br>Mali<br>Myanmar<br>Nepal | (1)<br>Togo | (12)<br>Afghanistan<br>Burundi<br>Chad<br>Ghana<br>Kenya<br>Liberia<br>Rwanda<br>Sierra Leone<br>Sudan<br>Zaire<br>Zambia<br>Zimbabwe |
| 45-55 (6) | (5)<br>China<br>Lesotho<br>Mauritania<br>Niger<br>Yemen | – | (1)<br>Mozambique |
| More than 55 (5) | (2)<br>Burkina Faso<br>United Rep. of<br>  Tanzania | – | (3)<br>Ethiopia, PDR<br>Haiti<br>Somalia |
| **Middle- to high-income countries (50)** | | | |
| Less than 15 (13) | (7)<br>Brazil<br>Hong Kong<br>Jordan<br>Korea, Rep.<br>Malaysia<br>Trinidad and<br>  Tobago<br>Turkey | (1)<br>United Arab<br>  Emirates | (5)<br>Argentina<br>Kuwait<br>Panama<br>Paraguay<br>Uruguay |

49

(continued)

(continued)

**TABLE 15**

| LEVEL AND APPARENT TREND IN PREVALENCE OF FOOD INADEQUACY[1] IN 98 DEVELOPING COUNTRIES, 1969-71 TO 1990-92 | | | |
|---|---|---|---|
| Prevalence of food inadequacy in 1969-71 | Trend in prevalence of food inadequacy, 1969-71 to 1990-92 | | |
| (Percentage) | Declined | Stable | Increased |
| 15-30 (19) | (13)<br>Costa Rica<br>Cuba<br>Korea, Dem.<br>  People's Rep.<br>Lebanon<br>Libyan Arab Jam.<br>Mexico<br>Morocco<br>Papua New Guinea<br>Swaziland<br>Syrian Arab Rep.<br>Thailand<br>Tunisia<br>Venezuela | (1)<br>Iraq | (5)<br>Cameroon<br>Chile<br>Jamaica<br>Peru<br>Senegal |
| 30-45 (14) | (13)<br>Bolivia<br>Botswana<br>Colombia<br>Congo<br>Dominican Rep.<br>Ecuador<br>Gabon<br>Guatemala<br>Indonesia<br>Iran, Islamic Rep.<br>Mauritius<br>Namibia<br>Suriname | – | (1)<br>Angola |
| 45-55 (4) | (4)<br>Algeria<br>El Salvador<br>Philippines<br>Saudi Arabia | – | – |
| More than 55 (0) | – | – | – |

[1] Proportion of population with inadequate access to food.
*Note:* Figures in parentheses refer to the number of countries.

inadequacy, i.e. they do not indicate to what degree the food available is inadequate. In order to capture this aspect, it is necessary to consider the gap or the distance between actual food availability and a required or target level. There are several ways in which this gap can be conceptualized: one is to consider the gap in relation to the underfed, comparing the actual per caput food consumption of the underfed people with a normative level. Another approach is to consider the gap in relation to the population as a whole and thus compare the actual per caput food supply of a country with the per caput supply level that would ensure a minimum prevalence of food inadequacy in the population.

A word of caution is in order regarding the interpretation of the estimates. Whether considering the food deficit on the basis of the underfed only or on that of the population as a whole, the elimination of these deficits will not necessarily suffice to ensure adequate access to food for everyone at some point in the *future*. Following are the main reasons why:

- The assessment of food inadequacy is based on estimates of energy requirements that refer to the prevailing age-sex distribution of the population concerned. As these distributions change over time, aggregate requirements will also change and so will the magnitude of food deficit to be eliminated.
- As the world adopts measures to improve conditions of health care and hygiene, future populations are likely to have higher statures and correspondingly higher body weights compared with present populations. Therefore, as the energy requirements used in the prevalence estimates are based on ideal body weights corresponding to the heights of the present population, the food deficits, as measured here, may not reflect future deficits.
- The deficits are expressed on a per caput basis, so the expected growth in population is not taken into account.

51

Consequently, the estimates of food deficit, or the implied "required" per caput food supply level presented here cannot be taken to indicate the full magnitude of the task that confronts the world if it is to solve the problem of inadequate access to food. Rather, they should be seen as an indicator of the task that remains on the food front under the *ceteris paribus* assumption that all other factors, including population and its age-sex distribution and the conditions of health care and hygiene, remain unchanged.

### Intensity of food inadequacy expressed as food deficit of the undernourished

When setting a normative level for calculating the food deficit in terms of the population with inadequate food access, the following points should be taken into consideration. It has been argued in this report that, for identifying individuals who have inadequate access to food, the cutoff point should be set at the lower end of the range of food requirements.

However, when choosing a normative level at which an individual's intake ought to be, this minimum requirement standard does not apply. Once people are free from the problem of food inadequacy, they are likely to choose different intake levels according to their needs within the whole range of variation in requirements. In this case, the average intake of these people will be roughly equal to the average requirement. (Some may of course decide to have an intake level above their own requirements, thus allowing themselves to become obese, but this cannot be a valid consideration while choosing a normative target.) Thus, the concept of freedom from food inadequacy points to the fact that the normative level should be set equal to the average requirement level.

Accordingly, the intensity of food inadequacy is based here on the difference between the actual per caput intake of the underfed and the average per caput requirement of the population. The average per caput energy requirements calculated for this purpose are based on body weights for adults and adolescents corresponding to a BMI of 22.0 (which is the average level of BMI observed among healthy, active people) and on activity allowances corresponding to the moderate activity norms of 1.78 x BMR (1.78 BMR) for males and 1.64 BMR for females. As regards children, the 5 percent extra allowance for desirable activity, which was previously excluded to calculate a minimum requirement, has been included for the present purpose.

The difference between the average requirement and the average intake of people with inadequate access to food is called quite simply the average food deficit of the undernourished. This difference multiplied by the number of people with inadequate food gives an estimate of the total food deficit. The total deficit expressed as a percentage of the DES is referred to as the *relative inadequacy* of the current food supply.

The average per caput energy consumption level of inadequately fed people and the calculated average per caput energy requirement for the different developing regions are given in Table 16.

The relative food inadequacy of the 98 developing countries considered in this study (see Table 17) declined by almost one-half in the 20 years since 1969-71. This is clearly a sign of progress, but the experience was not uniformly positive in all regions. In 1969-71, East and Southeast Asia had the largest relative food inadequacy level among all developing regions, followed by sub-Saharan Africa and South Asia. By 1990, the ranking had changed among these three regions, with sub-Saharan Africa not only emerging with the largest relative food inadequacy level but actually witnessing a rise contrary to the overall declining trend. There was also a slight increase in the 1980s in Latin America and the Caribbean although the relative inadequacy of food in this region was much lower than in sub-Saharan Africa.

**TABLE 16**

## AVERAGE PER CAPUT ENERGY CONSUMPTION OF UNDERNOURISHED POPULATION COMPARED WITH MINIMUM AND AVERAGE PER CAPUT ENERGY REQUIREMENTS

| Region | Average per caput energy consumption of undernourished population | | | Minimum per caput energy requirement | | | Average per caput energy requirement | | |
|---|---|---|---|---|---|---|---|---|---|
| | 1969-71 | 1979-81 | 1990-92 | 1969-71 | 1979-81 | 1990-92 | 1969-71 | 1979-81 | 1990-92 |
| *(kcal/day)* | | | | | | | | | |
| Sub-Saharan Africa | 1 490 | 1 480 | 1 470 | 1 810 | 1 810 | 1 800 | 2 110 | 2 100 | 2 100 |
| Near East and North Africa | 1 570 | 1 630 | 1 640 | 1 830 | 1 840 | 1 840 | 2 130 | 2 150 | 2 150 |
| East and Southeast Asia | 1 520 | 1 610 | 1 660 | 1 820 | 1 870 | 1 880 | 2 130 | 2 200 | 2 220 |
| South Asia | 1 530 | 1 540 | 1 580 | 1 770 | 1 780 | 1 790 | 2 070 | 2 090 | 2 110 |
| Latin America and the Caribbean | 1 610 | 1 650 | 1 660 | 1 830 | 1 850 | 1 870 | 2 140 | 2 170 | 2 200 |
| **Developing regions** | **1 530** | **1 580** | **1 610** | **1 810** | **1 830** | **1 840** | **2 110** | **2 150** | **2 170** |

53

It is remarkable how much progress was made by East and Southeast Asia. At the beginning of the two-decade period, its relative inadequacy was three times that of Latin America and the Caribbean, twice that of the Near East and North Africa and even more than that of Africa. Two decades later, it had almost caught up with Latin America and the Caribbean and the Near East and North Africa and had reduced its level of relative inadequacy to about one-third of sub-Saharan Africa's level – despite the fact that the average requirement rose the fastest in this region over the two decades because of changes in the age-sex composition of the population.

Table 18 (p. 57) shows the distribution of 98 developing countries classified according to their relative inadequacy ratios in 1969-71 and 1990-92. Although a number of countries shifted downwards to lower percentages, the number of countries with high percentages (10 percent or more) remained almost unchanged. Among the countries whose relative food deficit had been declining, China made considerable progress, with a reduction in the relative inadequacy of food supply from 14 percent in 1969-71 to about 4 percent in 1990-92. India also cut down its relative food inadequacy by almost half. In the Near East and North African countries, the relative inadequacy level almost reached zero (see Appendix 2, Table 7). Among the 14 countries in which the relative inadequacy of food supply was more than 15 percent in 1990-92, 11 are located in sub-Saharan Africa. Furthermore, among these countries, three (Ethiopia, PDR, Mozambique and Somalia) have been in this situation since 1969-71.

54

**FIGURE 6**

RELATIVE INADEQUACY OF FOOD SUPPLY IN 98 DEVELOPING COUNTRIES, 1969-71 AND 1990-92

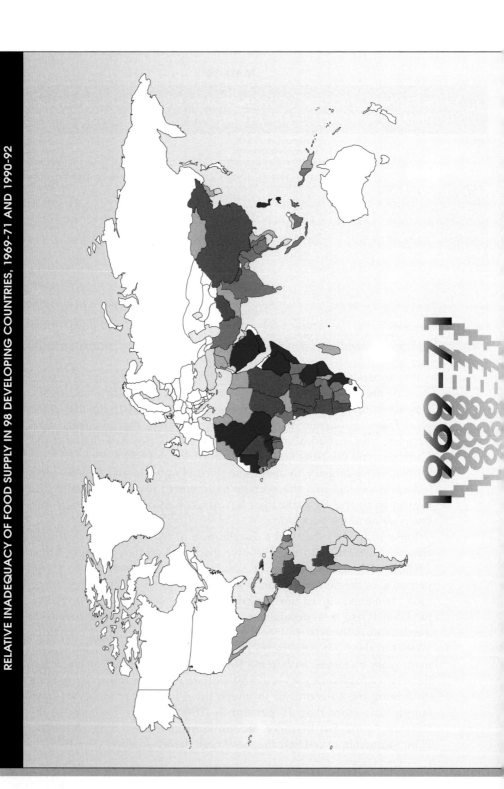

1969-71

1990-92

The food deficit situation has improved over the last 20 years, with particularly rapid declines in parts of Asia and the Near East and North Africa. However, critical food deficit persists in many parts of sub-Saharan Africa.

More than 15%

10-15%

7-10%

3-7%

Less than 3%

TABLE 17

**RELATIVE INADEQUACY OF FOOD SUPPLY BY DEVELOPING REGION, 1969-71, 1979-81 AND 1990-92**

| Region/economic group | Period | Per caput DES (kcal/day) | Relative inadequacy of food supply (Percentage) |
|---|---|---|---|
| **REGION** | | | |
| Sub-Saharan Africa | 1969-71 | 2 140 | 11 |
| | 1979-81 | 2 080 | 13 |
| | 1990-92 | 2 040 | 14 |
| Near East and North Africa | 1969-71 | 2 380 | 6 |
| | 1979-81 | 2 850 | 2 |
| | 1990-92 | 2 950 | 2 |
| East and Southeast Asia | 1969-71 | 2 060 | 12 |
| | 1979-81 | 2 370 | 7 |
| | 1990-92 | 2 680 | 3 |
| South Asia | 1969-71 | 2 060 | 9 |
| | 1979-81 | 2 070 | 9 |
| | 1990-92 | 2 290 | 5 |
| Latin America and the Caribbean | 1969-71 | 2 510 | 4 |
| | 1979-81 | 2 720 | 3 |
| | 1990-92 | 2 740 | 5 |
| **ECONOMIC GROUP** | | | |
| Low-income | 1969-71 | 2 060 | 11 |
| | 1979-81 | 2 210 | 9 |
| | 1990-92 | 2 430 | 6 |
| Middle- to high-income | 1969-71 | 2 360 | 6 |
| | 1979-81 | 2 670 | 3 |
| | 1990-92 | 2 760 | 3 |
| **Developing regions** | **1969-71** | **2 140** | **10** |
| | **1979-81** | **2 330** | **7** |
| | **1990-92** | **2 520** | **5** |

The countries where food inadequacy in 1990-92 could be characterized as critical are: Somalia (35 percent), Afghanistan (34 percent), Haiti (32 percent), Mozambique (29 percent), Ethiopia, PDR (28 percent), the Central African Republic (26 percent), Chad (25 percent), Liberia (23 percent), Sierra Leone (20 percent), Angola (20 percent), Burundi (18 percent), Malawi (16 percent), Peru (16 percent) and Kenya (15 percent).

It must be borne in mind that the absolute deficit underlying the above calculations of relative food inadequacy assumes that each underfed person obtains an additional amount of food equivalent to his or her own deficit, i.e. it assumes perfect targeting. However, in the absence of perfect targeting, there is no guarantee that the extra amount of food will be obtained by the underfed segment of the population. Its problem of food access is rooted in poverty and unequal distribution which would not be solved simply by making available on the market the amount of extra food calculated by this approach. In view of this, the following approach is considered.

## Intensity of food inadequacy expressed as food deficit of the total population

The food deficit of the population is defined here as the amount of additional food that would be needed in the aggregate to ensure that the present prevalence of food inadequacy in a population is practically eliminated (once again, under the *ceteris paribus* assumption). This total deficit would coincide with the relative food inadequacy only if it is assumed that all people with inadequate food access obtain extra food according to their respective requirement levels while the consumption of the rest of the population remains unchanged. It would not be realistic to expect such perfect targeting and the consequential compression of the intake distribution that this assumption implies. Therefore, when considering the elimination of the prevalence of food inadequacy in the population, it is necessary to make explicit assumptions about the intake distribution. To the extent that the assumption made about the intake distribution is deemed realistic, this procedure provides a better measure of the intensity of food inadequacy.

One extreme assumption could be that the inequality in the intake distribution is the same as the present one. This would be consistent with the *ceteris paribus* assumption but there is a serious obstacle to overcome in adopting this procedure. In many countries, the average consumption of the inadequately fed population is so low and the overall distribution so unequal that, if the required food supply is defined on the assumption of unchanged inequality, it would imply too high a level of intake at the

57

### TABLE 18

| DISTRIBUTION OF 98 DEVELOPING COUNTRIES CLASSIFIED ACCORDING TO THEIR RELATIVE INADEQUACY RATIOS, 1969-71 AND 1990-92 | | |
|---|---|---|
| Relative inadequacy of food supply | 1969-71 | 1990-92 |
| (Percentage) | (Number of countries) | |
| Less than 3 | 14 | 28 |
| 3-7 | 31 | 29 |
| 7-10 | 22 | 14 |
| 10-15 | 17 | 13 |
| More than 15 | 14 | 14 |
| | 98 | 98 |

upper end of the distribution (too high in the sense that it may be physiologically impossible to consume that amount of food, implying socially undesirable wastage, and that there would be a widespread problem of obesity if the more privileged were indeed to consume so much). A purely economic problem may also arise where there is no feasible price at which the more privileged, who are already close to the saturation point, will be induced to consume so much food. This means that, for the incremental food supply to be demanded at a feasible price, the distribution must be more even so the less privileged can gain additional purchasing power to generate the necessary demand. All these considerations suggest that, unless the average intake of a country is already quite high and the prevalence of food inadequacy relatively mild, it will not make sense to assume an unchanged distribution pattern.

To assess the per caput DES required to eliminate the prevalence of food inadequacy, it has to be assumed in general that the distribution contains less inequality than is actually the case. The degree of inequality in the distribution has been set at the minimum feasible level with a view to providing a lower limit estimate of the required food supply. If a higher degree of inequality is assumed, the required per caput food supply will be correspondingly higher.

Recent studies suggest that the CV of food consumption within a given population does not usually fall below 0.20, so this has been taken as the minimum feasible degree of inequality. Furthermore, elimination of the prevalence of food inadequacy has been taken to mean, in practical terms, a reduction of the prevalence of food inadequacy to 2.5 percent of the total population. The exact procedure of calculating the per caput DES on the basis of these assumptions is given in Appendix 3. The first step is to estimate the required per caput DES level for each country; that is, the per caput food supply level that would eliminate the prevalence of food inadequacy under the assumptions explained above. The difference between this required level and the actual per caput DES level gives the food deficit of the population.

Apart from calculating the required per caput DES level, an attempt was made in this survey to assess how far redistribution alone can tackle food inadequacy. A calculation was made of the prevalence of food inadequacy that would result from keeping the per caput DES at the present level while assuming a reduction of the CV to the level of 0.20. Depending on the scope for reducing the prevalence of food inadequacy through purely redistributive measures, countries are classified into four categories (Table 19) and the required per caput DES levels are then presented separately for each category (Table 20). This categorization allows cases in which redistribution can play a major role in eliminating food inadequacy to be distinguished from those in which an increase in the per caput DES must play a predominant role, and these cases, in turn, to be distinguished from those where there must be both an increase in per caput DES and redistribution. This point becomes clear from the following description of the four categories.

*Category 1.* The calculated prevalence of food inadequacy shows a rise rather than a decline from the currently assessed level. This indicates that the actual per caput DES levels in these countries are so low that some further growth is essential before redistribution measures can have a positive effect.

*Category 2.* The calculated prevalence of food inadequacy shows a decrease but this is less than half the currently assessed level. This indicates that the actual per caput DES levels in these countries are sufficiently high for redistribution to have a positive effect but not sufficiently high for redistribution to play a primary role.

*Category 3.* The calculated prevalence of food inadequacy shows a decrease by an amount equal to more than half the currently assessed level. This indicates that the actual per caput DES levels in these countries are sufficiently high to warrant a primary focus on redistribution measures.

*Category 4.* The decrease in the prevalence of food inadequacy is such that the new estimate is close to or lower than the target level of 2.5 percent of the total population. This indicates that the actual per caput DES levels are sufficiently high for redistribution to have a positive effect in eliminating the prevalence of food inadequacy without necessarily requiring further growth in the average consumption level.

The following salient points emerge from Table 20:

- The per caput DES levels required to eliminate the prevalence of food inadequacy are fairly close for all four country categories and average about 2 770 kcal/day. The small variations are explained by the differences in the stature and age-sex composition of the population adopted for calculating the minimum per caput energy requirement for the different countries.
- Moving from Category 1 to Category 4, the ratio of the required to the actual per caput DES levels declines consistently. This demonstrates the increasing role that redistribution can play as the per caput DES reaches higher levels.

**TABLE 19**

## CLASSIFICATION OF 98 DEVELOPING COUNTRIES
## INTO FOUR CATEGORIES BASED ON ROLES OF PER CAPUT DES
## GROWTH AND REDISTRIBUTION IN ELIMINATING FOOD INADEQUACY

**Category 1**

| | | |
|---|---|---|
| Afghanistan | Ethiopia, PDR | Mozambique |
| Central African Rep. | Haiti | Somalia |
| Chad | | |

**Category 2**

| | | |
|---|---|---|
| Angola | Kuwait | Panama |
| Bangladesh | Laos | Peru |
| Bolivia | Lesotho | Philippines |
| Burkina Faso | Liberia | Rwanda |
| Burundi | Madagascar | Sierra Leone |
| Cambodia | Malawi | Sri Lanka |
| Cameroon | Mali | Sudan |
| Congo | Mongolia | Trinidad and Tobago |
| Dominican Rep. | Namibia | United Rep. of Tanzania |
| Ghana | Nepal | Uruguay |
| Guyana | Nicaragua | Viet Nam |
| India | Niger | Zaire |
| Iraq | Nigeria | Zambia |
| Kenya | Pakistan | Zimbabwe |

**Category 3**

| | | |
|---|---|---|
| Benin | Gabon | Papua New Guinea |
| Botswana | Gambia | Senegal |
| Brazil | Guatemala | Suriname |
| Chile | Guinea | Swaziland |
| China | Honduras | Thailand |
| Colombia | Jamaica | Togo |
| Côte d'Ivoire | Mauritania | Uganda |
| Ecuador | Mauritius | Venezuela |
| El Salvador | Myanmar | Yemen |

**Category 4**

| | | |
|---|---|---|
| Algeria | Jordan | Morocco |
| Argentina | Korea, Dem. People's Rep. | Paraguay |
| Costa Rica | Korea, Rep. | Saudi Arabia |
| Cuba | Lebanon | Syrian Arab Rep. |
| Egypt | Libyan Arab Jam. | Tunisia |
| Hong Kong | Malaysia | Turkey |
| Indonesia | Mexico | United Arab Emirates |
| Iran, Islamic Rep. | | |

**TABLE 20**

### COMPARISON OF ACTUAL AND REQUIRED LEVELS OF PER CAPUT DES, 1990-92

| Country category | No. of countries in category | Actual per caput DES (kcal/day) | Required per caput DES (kcal/day) | Ratio of required to actual per caput DES |
|---|---|---|---|---|
| 1 | 7 | 1 660 | 2 730 | 1.6 |
| 2 | 42 | 2 240 | 2 700 | 1.2 |
| 3 | 27 | 2 680 | 2 860 | 1.1 |
| 4 | 22 | 3 000 | 2 780 | 0.9 |

- There are 22 countries (Category 4) where the present per caput DES levels are nearly as high or higher than the required levels, meaning their prevalence of food inadequacy could practically be eliminated through redistribution measures without any further increase in the per caput DES. However, for the large majority of countries (Categories 1, 2 and 3), an increase in per caput food supply will be needed in combination with redistribution measures. For the seven countries in Category 1, an increase in per caput DES levels is essential before redistribution can be effective.

61

# CHAPTER 3

# Assessment of child and adult undernutrition in developing countries

•

## Methodology for assessing undernutrition by anthropometry

•

## Anthropometric assessment of nutritional status

•

## Summary and conclusions

The assessment of nutritional inadequacy in the preceding chapter was concerned with the entire population of a country or a region. While such a global assessment has its uses, it is also sometimes necessary to consider specific groups within a population, especially those regarded as target groups for intervention purposes, for example children, women, old people or others who may warrant particular attention. However, when applied to such specific groups, the methodology adopted in the preceding chapter is limited by the fact that separate data on the dietary energy intakes of these population subgroups are seldom available on a sufficiently large scale. As a result, any exercise in group-specific assessment must rely on different data and a methodology that is more capable of assessing the status of individuals within a defined group. One such methodology is nutritional anthropometry.

This chapter uses the anthropometric assessment method to measure the nutritional inadequacy of children and adults in the developing countries. As explained in the Introduction, this method and the food adequacy approach differ conceptually and methodologically and therefore cannot be expected to provide the same estimates of the number of undernourished people. When applied to a country, the results generated by each approach would not add up to the same estimates for the entire population.[7] Strictly speaking, therefore, the assessment presented in this chapter cannot show for separate subgroups what the assessment in the preceding chapter showed for populations as a whole. Nonetheless, the anthropometric assessment is complementary to the results presented in the preceding chapter inasmuch as it focuses on the status of people in subgroups within a population.

To assist in the interpretation of these results, a detailed discussion on the advantages and limitations of anthropometry in the nutritional status assessment of both children and adults presented in Appendix 4, which also covers issues related to reference values and cutoff points for the classification of individuals. The cutoff points are based on established relationships between anthropometric indices, on the one hand, and functional impairments, augmented risks of morbidity and mortality and other evidence of the consequences of food and non-food risk factors, on the other. In other words, they are based on the fact that values of anthropometric indicators below the lower cutoff point are usually associated with a high incidence of the ill-effects of nutritional

---

[7] A further complication is that there are several alternative anthropometric indicators for children, each related to a different aspect of child undernutrition.

inadequacy, such as physical dysfunctions, morbidity and mortality. It is in this sense that people whose anthropometric indicators fall below the cutoff points are said to be at risk of being undernourished. A similar interpretation applies to the upper cutoff points used for identifying those at risk of being overnourished.

It should be stressed that, as in the case of the estimates of food inadequacy discussed in Chapter 2, the anthropometric approach generates probability estimates. Since the majority of individuals in the reference population are found to have anthropometric values that fall within the upper and lower cutoff points, it follows that the majority of those with anthropometric values outside the normal range are likely to be suffering from malnutrition. At the same time, a small proportion will be misclassified, i.e. classified as being malnourished when in fact they are not, and vice versa, even in the absence of measurement errors. The nutritional assessment is thus probabilistic.

## METHODOLOGY FOR ASSESSING UNDERNUTRITION BY ANTHROPOMETRY

The nutritional status of an individual or group of individuals can be assessed through the use of one or more anthropometric measurements to determine whether a person is likely to be well nourished or undernourished. This method generates objective measurements of body dimensions and composition as a proxy indicator of nutritional status. The most commonly used measurements of nutritional status assessment are based on growth and development in children and on body composition in adults.

Nutritional anthropometric indices have a number of advantages (see Box 2). However, they also have several limitations: i) day-to-day intra-individual variations in body weight may make it difficult to detect small weight losses owing to deficient energy intakes and/or increased health risks over short periods; ii) they are unable to distinguish the effects of specific nutrient deficiencies (such as zinc) that affect growth in children and induce changes in body composition from the effects of food and non-food risk factors; and iii) they are unable to detect the presence of undernutrition when it is manifested solely through a person's inability to undertake a desirable level of physical activity. As with most measurement techniques, there is also room for measurement errors, particularly if the survey personnel are not properly trained, although limitations on accurate age determination and sampling biases are perhaps potentially more serious sources of error.

The assessment of child and adult nutritional status is presented here in terms of two anthropometric measurements, weight and height, since these are the most widely applied indicators which allow highly specific and broadly accepted interpretations. Consequently, for a global assessment involving cross-region and cross-country comparisons, these two measurements are the most appropriate. A useful description of other anthropometric indicators (including their construction, application and interpretation) for children and adults may be found in WHO (1995) and Gibson (1990).

### Infants and children

The three most frequently used indicators to assess child nutritional status are based on height and weight: they are height for age, weight for height and weight for age. The *height for age* of a child reflects linear growth and measures long-term growth faltering or stunting, while *weight for height* adequately reflects body proportion. Weight for height is particularly sensitive to acute growth disturbances and indicates the presence of wasting. *Weight for age* represents a convenient synthesis of both linear growth and body proportion (WHO, 1986 and 1995).

The presence of undernutrition in children is diagnosed using these three anthropometric indicators and by comparing the measured values with the [United States] National Center for Health Statistics/WHO reference values (WHO, 1983). A normal or low-risk range is identified on the distribution curve of reference values. The two ends of the range are taken as cutoff points for identifying children with inadequate or excess nutrition. It is now generally agreed that the most appropriate cutoff points on the normalized distribution curve are: -2 SD or -2 Z-scores, to signal that the child is at risk of being *underweight* (weight for age), *stunted* (height for age) or *wasted* (weight for height). On a population basis, the prevalence of undernutrition for children under the

65

### BOX 2

### ANTHROPOMETRY AS AN INDICATOR OF NUTRITIONAL STATUS

Anthropometric indices provide an approximate reflection of the nutritional status of a community. They are useful indicators because they constitute:

- a simple and practical way of describing the problem;
- the best general proxy for constraints to human welfare, such as dietary inadequacies, infections and other environmental health risks;
- strong and feasible predictors, at individual and population levels, of the risks of subsequent morbidity, functional impairments and mortality;
- an appropriate indicator for measuring the success or failure of interventions.

*Source:* ACC/SCN (1990).

age of five is estimated by the proportion of children whose measurements fall below the cutoff points on the respective indices. In the same way, the prevalence of overweight children as a result of overnutrition is estimated by the proportion of children with a weight adjusted for height above +2 SD (or +2 Z-scores) on the normalized distribution curve.

### Older children and adolescents

The nutritional status in schoolchildren and adolescents is assessed by the same anthropometric indicators that are used for children under the age of five, i.e. weight for age, height for age and weight for height, and the same cutoff points (<-2 SD and >+2 SD of the NCHS/WHO reference values) are applied to classify schoolchildren and adolescents according to their risk of being malnourished. However, the same anthropometric indicators provide different information for children of different ages. For instance, a high prevalence of stunting among one-year-old children indicates the existence of current nutrition and health problems whereas, in children of five years or older, stunting reflects both past and current risks to growth and development. While the height indicator provides information about the past and present, indicators based on weight provide information about current processes. A proper interpretation of the actual nutrition situation of older children requires corroborating data related to food and diet, socio-economic status and the incidence of infectious diseases and parasitic infestation.

Adolescent nutritional status can also be assessed by a weight for height index, i.e. the BMI (weight [kg]/height$^2$ [m]). Adolescents with a BMI (adjusted for age) below the value corresponding to the 5th centile of the NCHS/WHO reference population are considered to be at risk of being undernourished (WHO, 1995). A BMI for age equal to or greater than that corresponding to the 85th centile indicates that an adolescent is at risk of being overweight. The estimated proportion of malnourished adolescents can be expected to be higher using the BMI and the indicated cutoff points than when using the -/+2 SD cutoff points, since the latter correspond to the 2.5th and 97.5th centiles of the respective distribution curves.

### Adults

Until recently, anthropometric assessments of nutritional status were carried out almost exclusively for children and adolescents because there was no satisfactory indicator of adult nutritional status available. However, much progress has been made over these last years in identifying such an indicator, and the BMI (weight/height$^2$) is considered at present to be the most suitable anthropometric indicator of adult nutritional status (Shetty and James in FAO, 1994b; Ferro-Luzzi *et al.*, 1992; James, Ferro-Luzzi and Waterlow, 1988). The advantage of this indicator is that, while being consistently and highly correlated with body weight (or body energy stores), it is also relatively independent of adult stature so it permits a comparison of body proportion across population groups of varying statures (see Appendix 4).

A low BMI value reflects both low body fat and muscle mass for a given height. It has been argued that age, gender, body shape and ethnicity should be taken into account when interpreting BMI values in terms of body composition (Norgan, 1994), although in healthy populations the variations in BMI owing to such factors are likely to be small (Shetty and James in FAO, 1994b). Thus, if the observed BMI of an individual is found to lie below the lower end of a normal range of variation, there is a high risk that the person is suffering from the ill-effects of chronic nutritional deficiency (principally, chronic energy deficiency [CED]). Accordingly, the lower end of the range of normal variation is used as the cutoff point for the diagnosis of chronic undernutrition in adults. On the basis of current knowledge, the best estimate of this critical point is 18.5 (WHO, 1995) (see Appendix 4 for a more detailed explanation).

The lower limit of normality (the BMI value of 18.5) was established from the observation of BMI values of a large sample of male soldiers and healthy women in the United Kingdom (Shetty and James in FAO, 1994b). The universal application of the reference population and of the cutoff point of BMI 18.5 to other populations has been questioned (Garcia and Kennedy, 1994; Norgan, 1990 and 1994; Immink, Flores and Diaz, 1992). However, in the absence of more consistent data from different countries and population groups, this cutoff point has been accepted for the time being, among other reasons to facilitate cross-country comparisons. Concerns that lean but healthy and very active adults may be wrongly classified as undernourished initially resulted in the inclusion of energy turnover based on the BMR as an additional criterion but the BMI alone is now accepted as an anthropometric indicator of chronic adult undernutrition, since the numbers likely to be misclassified in a representative population sample are considered to be insignificant (James and François, 1994).

The BMI can also be used to assess overnutrition in adults, and specific cutoff points are applied for classifying people as overweight (25.0-29.9: obesity grade 1) or frankly obese (30.0-39.9: obesity grade 2; ≥40.0: obesity grade 3). The universal application of BMI 25.0 as the cutoff point to define obesity has also been questioned and it has been suggested that population-specific cutoff points and country-specific reference populations be established.

Using the BMI as an anthropometric indicator of adult nutrition has similar advantages to weight adjusted for height in children: it reflects the degree of severity of under- and overnutrition while height and weight data – the basic data from which the BMI is constructed – can readily be incorporated into ongoing national surveys. Finally, since the BMI is relatively independent of stature, its use permits comparative analyses of various kinds, for example between functional classifications (such as age-group, rural-urban location, occupation) as well as inter-regional and intercountry comparisons.

## ANTHROPOMETRIC ASSESSMENT OF NUTRITIONAL STATUS

This section presents available estimates of the nutritional status of children, adolescents and adults, using the anthropometric indicators described above. The estimates are given in terms of the prevalence of undernutrition in different countries and regions and have been derived using the appropriate cutoff points and reference values.[8] Country data with the most recent prevalence of underweight, stunted and wasted children under five are found in Appendix 2, Table 8. For a limited number of countries, the prevalence of obesity (>2 SD) in the under-five group is also listed. The data available only permit global estimates for children under five while, for schoolchildren, adolescents and adults, data are given only for a limited number of countries.

### Undernutrition in children under five: the current situation

The basic data on the anthropometry of children under the age of five are obtained from WHO's Global Database on Child Growth, which was initiated in 1986 for the purpose of compiling, systematizing and disseminating the results of representative anthropometric surveys in different parts of the world (de Onis *et al.*, 1993). Estimated *proportions* of underweight, stunted and wasted children under five are derived from this database and then applied to population estimates for 1990 in order to obtain the absolute *numbers.*

The results of this analysis are presented in Table 21 for broad regions of the developing world.[9] According to these estimates, two out of five children in the developing world are stunted (low height for age), one out

---

[8] Like the food inadequacy approach discussed in the Introduction, anthropometry will also tend to underestimate the true prevalence of undernutrition, although for different reasons.

[9] The data for individual countries are presented in Appendix 2, Table 8.

TABLE 21

## ESTIMATES OF PREVALENCE AND NUMBERS OF WASTED, STUNTED AND UNDERWEIGHT CHILDREN IN DEVELOPING COUNTRIES, 1990

| Region/economic group | Wasted | | Stunted | | Underweight | | Total number of children under five |
|---|---|---|---|---|---|---|---|
| | Percentage | Number (Millions) | Percentage | Number (Millions) | Percentage | Number (Millions) | (Millions) |
| **REGION** | | | | | | | |
| Sub-Saharan Africa | 7 | 6 | 38 | 34 | 30 | 26 | 88 |
| Near East and North Africa | 9 | 4 | 32 | 16 | 25 | 12 | 49 |
| South Asia | 17 | 27 | 60 | 93 | 58 | 91 | 156 |
| East and Southeast Asia | 5 | 9 | 33 | 60 | 24 | 42 | 180 |
| Latin America and the Caribbean | 3 | 1 | 23 | 12 | 12 | 6 | 55 |
| **ECONOMIC GROUP** | | | | | | | |
| Low-income | 10 | 40 | 45 | 175 | 38 | 148 | 388 |
| Middle- to high-income | 6 | 8 | 29 | 40 | 22 | 31 | 140 |
| **Total** | **9** | **48** | **41** | **215** | **34** | **179** | **528** |

Source: WHO Global Database on Child Growth, available as of December 1995.

69

of three is underweight (low weight for age) and one out of ten is wasted (low weight for height). In absolute numbers, there were 215 million stunted children, 179 million underweight and nearly 50 million wasted children in 1990.

The proportions of children under five suffering from undernutrition vary significantly among regions: South Asia has the highest proportions of underweight, stunted and wasted children while at the other end of the scale is Latin America and the Caribbean.

South Asia's combination of the highest incidence of undernutrition and a large population makes it the home of an overwhelming majority of the undernourished children in the developing world: it accounts for 50 percent of all underweight children, 43 percent of stunted children and 56 percent of wasted children in developing countries (Figure 7).

Given that South Asia has a 30 percent share of all children under the age of five in the developing countries, these figures indicate that the region has a disproportionately large share of undernourished children. By contrast, with an 11 percent share of the children under five in the developing countries, Latin America and the Caribbean has only 4 percent of the underweight, 6 percent of the stunted and 3 percent of the wasted children. Similarly, with 22 percent of the children under five, China has only 11 percent of the underweight, 17 percent of the stunted and 8 percent of the wasted children. In East and Southeast Asia, the proportions of undernourished children (12 percent underweight, 11 percent stunted and 11 percent wasted) are quite similar to this region's share of the developing countries' population under the age of five (12 percent), and the same is true for sub-Saharan Africa and the countries of the Near East and North Africa.

**FIGURE 7**

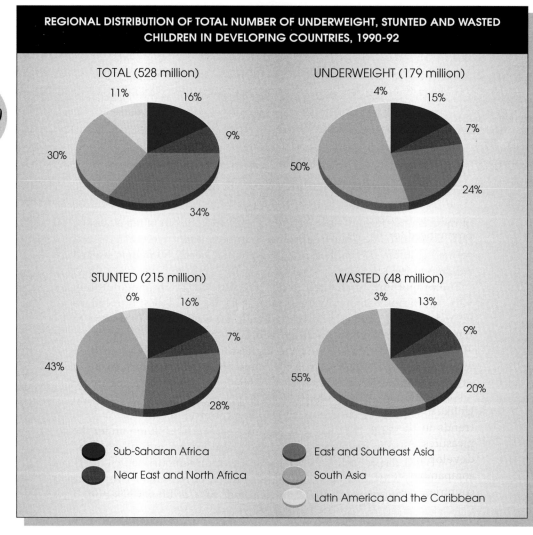

REGIONAL DISTRIBUTION OF TOTAL NUMBER OF UNDERWEIGHT, STUNTED AND WASTED CHILDREN IN DEVELOPING COUNTRIES, 1990-92

TOTAL (528 million)

UNDERWEIGHT (179 million)

STUNTED (215 million)

WASTED (48 million)

Sub-Saharan Africa

East and Southeast Asia

Near East and North Africa

South Asia

Latin America and the Caribbean

An analysis based on the two-way classification of the developing countries into low-income and middle- to high-income groups revealed the following picture (see also Table 21). The average prevalence of underweight, stunted and wasted children was substantially higher in the low-income countries, at 38, 45 and 10 percent, respectively, compared with 22, 29 and 6 percent in the middle- to high-income group. The vast majority of undernourished children also live in the low-income countries, as do 73 percent of the total population of children under five in the developing world and more than 80 percent of the undernourished children (83 percent of the underweight, 81 percent of the stunted and 83 percent of the wasted children). Thus, the low-income countries have disproportionately high shares of underweight, stunted and wasted children.

In each of the regions, low-income countries as a group have a generally higher prevalence of undernutrition than middle- to high-income countries. The glaring exception in Southeast Asia is China. Also, only small differences in the prevalence of wasting is found between low-income and middle- to high-income countries in Latin America and the Caribbean (where the prevalence of child undernutrition is relatively low overall) and in the Near East and North Africa.

Among the low-income countries, the sharpest regional variation is found in the prevalence of underweight children as compared with the prevalence of stunting and wasting. For example, the proportion of underweight children varies from 58 percent in South Asia to 17 percent in China, whereas the proportion of wasting ranges from 17 percent in South Asia to 3 percent in Latin America and the Caribbean. Among the middle- to high-income countries, the interregional variation is much less pronounced for all three indicators.

In a small number of countries for which the information is available, the prevalence of obesity in children under five exceeds the prevalence expected in a healthy population, i.e. 2.5 percent (Appendix 2, Table 8). This is true for 11 out of the total of 22 countries with data available. In these 11 countries, the prevalence of underweight children is relatively low, although there are some notable exceptions such as China, Egypt and Mauritius. This points to a certain degree of coexistence of under- and overnutrition in some countries, as is also the case among adults.

**Undernutrition in children under five: changes over time**

Unlike in the case of food inadequacy, it is difficult to determine long-term trends in the prevalence of undernutrition based on anthropometric measures. At best, changes that have occurred over time in a number of developing countries can be analysed. This is because repeated and comparable surveys for different points in time are not available for most countries. Nevertheless, WHO has made a systematic attempt to compile and collate the findings of as many surveys as possible even though they are not always comparable within the same country and often differ in terms of methodology, sample frame, sample size, etc. Particularly limiting is the fact that repeated surveys do not always cover the same age group. For purposes of intercountry comparisons, an additional problem is that the time span covered by the repeated surveys is not identical for each country – in some cases the period extends from the mid-1970s to the early or mid-1990s whereas, in others, it covers only a part of the 1980s. Bearing these caveats in mind, some indication about the nature of change over time can be obtained from the data assembled in Table 22, which shows the direction in which the proportion of underweight children has changed according to repeated surveys in individual countries.

**TABLE 22**

**CHANGE OVER TIME IN THE PREVALENCE OF UNDERWEIGHT CHILDREN (UNDER 5 YEARS) IN SELECTED DEVELOPING COUNTRIES**

| Region/country | Survey year | Underweight children under 5 years | |
| --- | --- | --- | --- |
| | | Prevalence (Percentage) | Change over time |
| **Sub-Saharan Africa** | | | |
| Ethiopia, PDR | 1982, 1992[1,5] | 38.1, 47.7 | ↗ |
| Ghana | 1988, 1994[2] | 27.1, 27.4 | — |
| Kenya | 1982,[1] 1987,[1] 1993 | 22.0, 18.0, 22.3 | ↘↗ |
| Lesotho | 1976, 1981, 1992 | 17.3, 13.3, 15.8 | ↘↗ |
| Madagascar | 1984, 1992 | 32.8, 39.1 | ↗ |
| Malawi | 1981, 1992 | 23.9, 27.2 | ↗ |
| Mauritania | 1981, 1991 | 31.0, 47.6 | ↗ |
| Rwanda | 1976, 1985, 1992 | 27.8, 27.5, 29.2 | —↗ |
| Senegal | 1986,[5] 1993 | 17.5, 20.1 | ↗ |
| Sierra Leone | 1975, 1978, 1990 | 31.0, 23.2, 28.7 | ↘↗ |
| Togo | 1977,[5] 1988[3] | 20.5, 24.4 | ↗ |
| Zambia | 1985, 1988, 1992 | 20.5, 25.8, 25.1 | ↗— |
| Zimbabwe | 1984, 1988,[5] 1994 | 20.7, 10.0, 15.5 | ↘↗ |
| **Near East and North Africa** | | | |
| Algeria | 1987, 1990, 1992 | 8.6, 9.2, 9.2 | — |
| Egypt | 1978, 1990, 1992, 1995[7] | 16.6, 10.4, 9.4, 16.8 | ↘↗ |
| Jordan | 1975, 1990 | 17.4, 6.4 | ↘ |
| Morocco | 1987,[5] 1992 | 11.8, 9.0 | ↘ |
| Tunisia | 1975, 1988[8] | 20.2, 10.4 | ↘ |

*(continued)*

*(continued)* **TABLE 22**

| CHANGE OVER TIME IN THE PREVALENCE OF UNDERWEIGHT CHILDREN (UNDER 5 YEARS) IN SELECTED DEVELOPING COUNTRIES | | | |
|---|---|---|---|
| **Region/country** | **Survey year** | **Underweight children under 5 years** | |
| | | **Prevalence** (Percentage) | **Change over time** |
| **Latin America and the Caribbean** | | | |
| Bolivia | 1981, 1989,[5] 1994[8] | 14.5, 11.4, 15.7 | ↘↗ |
| Brazil | 1975, 1989 | 18.4, 7.0 | ↘ |
| Chile | 1978, 1982, 1986, 1994 | 2.1, 1.1, 2.5, 0.9 | — |
| Colombia | 1980, 1986,[5] 1989 | 16.7, 10.2, 10.1 | ↘— |
| Costa Rica | 1978, 1982, 1992[9] | 16.0, 6.0, 2.3 | ↘ |
| Dominican Rep. | 1986, 1991 | 12.5, 10.4 | ↘ |
| El Salvador | 1975, 1988, 1993[6] | 21.6, 15.5, 11.2 | ↘ |
| Guatemala | 1980, 1987[8] | 43.6, 33.5 | ↘ |
| Haiti | 1978, 1990[6] | 37.4, 33.9 | ↘ |
| Honduras | 1987, 1992 | 20.6, 19.3 | ↘ |
| Jamaica | 1978, 1985, 1989 | 15.0, 14.9, 7.2 | ↘ |
| Mexico | 1988, 1989[10] | 13.9, 19.0 | ↗ |
| Nicaragua | 1981, 1993 | 10.5, 11.9 | ↗ |
| Panama | 1980, 1992 | 15.7, 6.1 | ↘ |
| Peru | 1975, 1984, 1992 | 16.1, 13.4, 10.8 | ↘ |
| Trinidad and Tobago | 1976, 1987[8] | 16.3, 6.9 | ↘ |
| **South Asia** | | | |
| Bangladesh | 1975, 1981, 1985, 1990[4] | 84.4, 70.1, 71.5, 65.8 | ↘ |
| India | 1977,[9] 1989,[9] 1992 | 78.0, 69.0, 61.0 | ↘ |
| Pakistan | 1977, 1986 1991 | 54.7, 48.8, 40.4 | ↘ |
| Sri Lanka | 1976, 1980, 1987[8] | 58.3, 47.5, 38.1 | ↘ |
| **Southeast Asia** | | | |
| China | 1987,[2] 1992 | 21.3, 17.4 | ↘ |
| Laos | 1984, 1994 | 36.5, 40.0 | ↗ |
| Malaysia | 1983, 1986, 1993 | 25.6, 17.1, 23.3 | ↘↗ |
| Myanmar | 1982, 1987, 1990, 1991[3] | 42.0, 42.0, 32.4, 36.7 | ↘↗ |
| Philippines | 1982, 1987, 1992, 1993 | 33.2, 32.9, 33.4, 29.6 | —↘ |
| Thailand | 1982, 1987,[8] 1990 | 36.0, 25.8, 13.0 | ↘ |
| Viet Nam | 1986, 1989, 1994 | 51.5, 41.9, 44.9 | ↘↗ |

[1] Rural areas only.
[2] Excludes some districts, provinces or zones.
[3] 0-35 months.
[4] 6-59 months.
[5] 6-36 months, adjusted 0-59 m.
[6] Adjusted for misreporting of age.
[7] 6-71 months.
[8] 3-36 months.
[9] 12-72 months.
[10] 12-59 months, rural areas.

*Sources:* ACC/SCN (1987; 1989; 1992; 1994) and WHO Global Database on Child Growth.

73

The overall picture is one of a varied pattern of change in the proportion of underweight children. Even within a number of countries, the pattern of change is not consistent. Among the 45 developing countries included, 20 show a somewhat consistent pattern of decline in the prevalence of child undernutrition while about half of these again (11) are located in Latin America and the Caribbean. All the four countries in South Asia, three of the seven Southeast Asian countries and three of the five countries in the Near East and North Africa also show a declining prevalence over time. However, in sub-Saharan Africa, almost all the countries show an increasing prevalence.

### Undernutrition in schoolchildren

Because of the paucity of data, only general statements can be made about the prevalence of undernutrition in schoolchildren in specific developing countries. This is especially true of some Latin American countries, where the heights of all first grade students between the ages of six and nine were measured on a national basis. The periodic implementation of these national surveys, as has been done in Costa Rica and Panama for example, provides a picture of change over time (Table 23). In Costa Rica, the prevalence of stunting declined over time while, in Panama, after declining in the first half of the 1980s, stunting among schoolchildren tended to increase during the second half of the decade.

### Undernutrition in adolescents and adults

Globally, representative data on adolescent nutritional status are generally lacking. Table 24 summarizes data compiled by Kurz and Johnson-Welch (1994) on stunting and thinness in both male and female adolescents of selected countries.[10] These data indicate significant intercountry differences in the proportion of stunted and thin adolescents, both among males and females. The comparability of these data sets is too limited to permit more precise statements on intercountry patterns but observations can be made regarding the pattern of gender differentials. First, while female adolescents suffer from more than twice as much stunting as males in India, the opposite is true in the two African countries, Benin and Cameroon. Second, the gender differential in thinness (low BMI for age) appears to have a uniform pattern everywhere – male adolescents have a consistently

---

[10] It should be noted that the cutoff points used in this study to define stunting (low height for age) and thinness (low BMI for age) differ slightly from those currently recommended by WHO (1995).

**TABLE 23**

### PREVALENCE OF STUNTING INDICATED BY NATIONAL HEIGHT SURVEYS AMONG SCHOOLCHILDREN IN LATIN AMERICA AND THE CARIBBEAN

| Country | Survey year | Prevalence of stunting among children of 6-9 years |
|---|---|---|
| | | *(Percentage)* |
| Argentina | 1985 | 10.0 |
| Bolivia | 1988-90 | 35.0 |
| Chile | 1990 | 27.5-28.6[1] |
| Costa Rica | 1979 | 20.4 |
| | 1981 | 15.5 |
| | 1983 | 12.6 |
| | 1985 | 11.3 |
| | 1989 | 9.2 |
| Dominican Rep. | 1993 | 19.0 |
| El Salvador | 1988 | 30.0 |
| Guatemala | 1986 | 37.4 |
| Honduras | 1986 | 40.0 |
| Nicaragua | 1986 | 23.9 |
| | 1989 | 18.7 |
| Panama | 1982 | 23.1 |
| | 1985 | 18.8 |
| | 1988 | 24.4 |
| Paraguay[2] | 1988 | 9.3 |
| Uruguay | 1987 | 4.0 |
| | 1990 | 4.1 |

[1] Below the 10th centile of the NCHS/WHO reference values.
[2] Seven to 14 years of age.

*Source:* International Conference on Nutrition background country papers.

higher prevalence of thinness than female adolescents. Third, the high prevalence of thinness in both female and male adolescents in India and Nepal stands out in comparison with the other countries.

As mentioned before, the anthropometric assessment of adult nutritional status is a relatively new phenomenon. As a result, there are very few data sets, although BMI data for adults are now becoming increasingly available. Table 25 summarizes some of the available data based on representative surveys from different countries and geographical regions of the developing world, revealing the coexistence of adult under- and overnutrition (see also Box 3, p. 78). In Latin

**TABLE 24**

### PREVALENCE OF STUNTING AND THINNESS AMONG ADOLESCENT MALES AND FEMALES IN SELECTED COUNTRIES

| Country | Stunted[1] | | | Thin[2] | | |
|---|---|---|---|---|---|---|
| | All | Males | Females | All | Males | Females |
| | | | (Percentage) | | | |
| Benin | 41 | 55 | 27 | 23 | 32 | 14 |
| Cameroon | 12 | 19 | 8 | 4 | 7 | 2 |
| Ecuador | 50 | ... | ... | 9 | 13 | 6 |
| Guatemala | 57 | ... | ... | 4 | ... | ... |
| India | 32 | 20 | 45 | 55 | 69 | 37 |
| Jamaica | 2 | ... | ... | 3 | ... | ... |
| Mexico | 62 | ... | ... | 3 | ... | ... |
| Nepal | 47 | ... | ... | 36 | 49 | 25 |
| Philippines (Cebu) | 43 | ... | ... | 13 | 19 | 7 |
| Philippines (Mindanao) | 65 | ... | ... | 6 | 9 | 1 |

[1] Low height for age, defined as below the 5th percentile of the NCHS/WHO reference values. The recent WHO report (WHO, 1995) recommends below the 3rd percentile or -2 Z-scores as appropriate.
[2] Low BMI for age, defined as below the 5th percentile of the BMI for age.

*Source:* Kurz and Johnson-Welch (1994).

American countries the proportion of underweight adults is small; in fact, there is a strong tendency for adults to be overweight, tending particularly towards obesity grade 1. Among African adults, the proportion of those underweight is greater in the Sahelian countries than in tropical or subtropical areas, while the proportion of overweight adults on the continent as a whole tends to be significantly lower than in Latin America.

A relatively large proportion of adults in Asia have a BMI under the minimum acceptable level of 18.5, for example 12.5 percent in China, 16.9 percent in Laos and a staggering 48.6 percent in India. The proportion of adults found to be in the normal range of variation of BMI (18.5 to 25.0) in China and Laos approximates that in many African countries, but not so in India where the proportion is significantly lower. The prevalence of adult obesity in Asia is in general the lowest among the developing regions.

**TABLE 25**

| Country | BMI categories | | | | | | Mean | No. of adults | Survey year |
|---|---|---|---|---|---|---|---|---|---|
| | <16.00 | 16.00-16.99 | 17.00-18.49 | 18.50-24.99 | 25.00-29.99 | ≥30.00 | | | |
| **Africa[1]** | | | | | | | | | |
| Congo[2] | 0.6 | 1.8 | 8.7 | 73.7 | 11.8 | 3.4 | 23.10 | 2 295 | 1986-87 |
| Ghana | 2.8 | 3.9 | 13.3 | 62.0 | 17.1 | 0.9 | ... | 6 323 | 1987-88 |
| Ghana[2] | 0.8 | 1.7 | 8.7 | 75.9 | 9.7 | 3.2 | 21.79 | 1 833 | 1993 |
| Kenya[2] | 0.5 | 1.3 | 7.4 | 76.8 | 11.5 | 2.4 | 22.04 | 3 547 | 1993 |
| Mali | 1.9 | 3.2 | 11.2 | 76.5 | 6.4 | 0.8 | 21.10 | 4 868 | 1991 |
| Morocco | 0.5 | 1.1 | 5.4 | 69.1 | 18.7 | 5.2 | 22.97 | 41 921 | 1984-85 |
| Morocco[2] | 0.3 | 0.5 | 2.8 | 62.0 | 23.3 | 11.1 | 24.27 | 3 234 | 1992 |
| Senegal | 1.4 | 2.0 | 10.2 | 70.4 | 12.2 | 3.7 | 21.94 | 3 241 | 1992-93 |
| Tunisia | 0.3 | 0.6 | 3.0 | 58.9 | 28.6 | 8.6 | 24.25 | 10 023 | 1990 |
| Zambia[2] | 0.0 | 1.1 | 6.0 | 70.3 | 16.9 | 5.7 | 22.91 | 350[3] | 1992 |
| **Latin America and the Caribbean** | | | | | | | | | |
| Brazil | 0.5 | 0.9 | 4.2 | 61.7 | 25.1 | 8.6 | (22.8, 23.2) | 32 381 | 1989 |
| Cuba | 0.6 | 1.3 | 5.4 | 56.3 | 26.9 | 9.5 | ... | 30 363 | 1982 |
| Peru | 0.2 | 0.2 | 2.6 | 63.2 | 24.8 | 9.0 | ... | 3 145 | 1975-76 |
| **Asia** | | | | | | | | | |
| China | 1.0 | 3.9 | 7.4 | 79.5 | 7.2 | 1.0 | 20.98 | 13 387 | 1982 |
| India | 10.2 | 12.7 | 25.7 | 47.9 | 3.0 | 0.5 | ... | 21 361 | 1988-90 |
| Laos | 1.6 | 2.9 | 11.4 | 76.9 | 6.5 | 0.7 | 20.94 | 7 138 | 1994 |

[1] This classification refers to continental Africa, hence the inclusion of Morocco and Tunisia.
[2] Women only.
[3] Part of data set only.

*Sources:* IRD/Macro International Inc., Demographic and Health Surveys 1992 and 1993; Shetty and James in FAO (1994b).

77

## SUMMARY AND CONCLUSIONS

The most frequently employed indicators of undernutrition in children (0 to ten years) are weight for age, height for age and weight for height. Children are classified according to their nutritional status by comparing their measurements with reference values for a normal healthy population and with specific cutoff values of the normalized distribution for that population.

**BOX 3**

## NUTRITION PARADOX: COEXISTENCE OF LOW BODY WEIGHT AND OBESITY IN DEVELOPING COUNTRIES

The apparent paradox of the coexistence of undernutrition and overnutrition (as manifested in obesity) is being increasingly recognized because of its implications for nutrition policy. In a number of developing countries with relatively low per caput incomes, the prevalence of obesity among adults, particularly in urban areas, is often found to be surprisingly high. Prevalence figures for obesity grade 1 (25 ≤BMI <30.0) in some Latin American countries are often similar to those for some European countries and the United States, although figures for obesity grade 2 (BMI ≥30.0) are still somewhat lower. Furthermore, the prevalence of obesity among adults is often a multiple of the prevalence of weight deficiency.

The prevalence of obesity (weight for height >120 percent) reported for individuals over 15 years of age in a number of Caribbean countries in the 1970s and 1980s ranged from 6 to 21 percent among men and from 22 to 48 percent among women. In African countries[1] such as the Congo, Ghana, Mali, Morocco and Tunisia, during the 1980s the prevalence of obesity grade 1 was found to range from 6.4 percent (Mali) to 28.6 percent (Tunisia), and the prevalence of obesity grade 2 from 0.8 percent to 8.6 percent. Only in Asia is the problem still insignificant from a public health point of view.

Recent evidence from China and the urban Congo shows that the prevalence of obesity among adult men and women increases with income while the proportions of underweight as well as normal-weight adults decline. However, manifestations of under- and overnutrition coexist to some extent at all income levels.

Anthropometric data from Senegal and the Congo on children under five and their mothers are particularly revealing in demonstrating the nutrition paradox. In a rural population in Senegal, 3.6 percent and 18.9 percent of children under five were, respectively, wasted and stunted. Among their mothers, 6 percent were underweight (BMI <18.5) and 8.6 percent were overweight (BMI >25.0). Similarly, in the Congo, while 5.6 percent and 27.5 percent of rural children under five were respectively wasted and stunted, among their mothers 13 percent were underweight and 8.6 percent were overweight. A similar phenomenon of the coexistence of weight deficiency and obesity among mothers of undernourished children was also observed in the urban populations of both countries.

---

[1] Continental Africa, hence the reference to Morocco and Tunisia.

*Source:* Delpeuch (1995).

The cutoff points are based on an augmented risk of morbidity and mortality and, for all three indicators, are: <-2 SD = undernourished and >+2 SD = overweight (weight indicators only). In adults, the currently favoured indicator is the BMI (weight [kg]/height$^2$ [m]) which is used for assessing both undernutrition (<18.5) and obesity (≥25.0). The interpretation of the weight and height indices for children is relatively simple but the interpretation of the BMI for adults is more complex. It is estimated that, in 1990, there were 179 million children under five who were weight-deficient, 215 million who were stunted and 48 million who were wasted in the developing countries. Of the total population under five years of age, 41 percent were stunted, 34 percent were underweight and 9 percent were wasted. The highest proportions were found in South Asia, followed by sub-Saharan Africa. This ranking is the reverse of the one based on the prevalence of food inadequacy discussed in Chapter 2. A plausible explanation for this reversal is based on the differences in disease environments: a high population density combined with a monsoon climate makes the spread of diseases – especially the water-borne kinds – much easier and much more lethal in South Asia than in sub-Saharan Africa. As a result, the children of South Asia are much more susceptible to nutritional stress in spite of a lower overall prevalence of food inadequacy in this region. The combination of a high rate of undernutrition and a large population size makes South Asia the home of by far the largest number of undernourished children in the developing regions. Overall, in 1990, 80 percent of the world's undernourished children lived in Asia (mostly in South Asia), 15 percent in Africa and 5 percent in Latin America.

Globally, there is an indication that the prevalence of weight deficiency among children under five is declining over time in a number of countries. The pattern is strongest in South Asia and Latin America, while the prevalence of weight deficiency is actually increasing in sub-Saharan Africa and the situation in the remaining regions is mixed. Global assessments of the nutritional status of schoolchildren and adolescents are impossible since little empirical evidence can be drawn from national surveys.

Data on the BMI for adults are not widely available for developing countries. Evidence from selected countries reveals that adult undernutrition, as indicated by a BMI value of less than 18.5, is often less prevalent than manifestations of overnutrition (except in South Asia), as indicated by a BMI value greater than 25.0. The prevalence of adult obesity is generally highest in Latin America and lowest in Asia. Women tend to be more affected by obesity than men and obesity is more prevalent in urban than rural areas. More and more, one can observe the coexistence of under- and overnutrition among children and adults in the developing countries, which points to a process of "nutritional transition". Increased urbanization, changing food intake patterns and lifestyles as well as general economic growth all contribute to a gradual shift towards overnutrition, while undernutrition remains highly prevalent. It should be noted, however, that this shift is still barely evident in countries with very low levels of per caput income.

# CHAPTER 4

# Concluding observations: varieties of deprivation

This survey has concentrated mainly on food, i.e. the problems related to both its quality and quantity or, more specifically, its excess or inadequate consumption. While the study has dwelt on both aspects, for obvious reasons the emphasis has been on the problem of inadequate food access in large parts of the developing world.

World availability of food, as measured by per caput DES, increased by over one-tenth in the two decades between 1969-71 and 1990-92. More impressive was the achievement of the developing countries as a group, where per caput DES increased by almost one-fifth. Despite such progress made in improving the aggregate availability of food, one in every five people had inadequate access to food in the developing world at the start of the present decade. In absolute numbers, this translates into about 800 million people without access to adequate food.

These figures, however, indicate a certain improvement over the situation two decades ago when one person in three in the developing regions – with a total population of about 900 million – had inadequate access to food. The most significant improvement occurred in Asia, especially East and Southeast Asia, and to a lesser extent in the low-income countries of South Asia. Nevertheless, the overall scale of the food inadequacy problem remains enormous. What is more, hardly any progress was made in large parts of the world, especially in sub-Saharan Africa where the proportion of population with inadequate food increased slightly and the absolute number almost doubled in the two decades starting from 1969-71. Latin America and the Caribbean also faced hardship in the "lost decade" of the 1980s, when the proportion of the population with inadequate food remained practically constant and the absolute number increased by about one-third.

Food deprivation is a major contributor to the broader problem of undernutrition that besets much of the developing world and parts of the developed world as well. At the start of the present decade, two out of five children under the age of five in the developing world were stunted (low height for age), one out of three was underweight (low weight for age) and one out of ten was wasted (low weight for height). In absolute numbers,[11] about 200 million children under five in the developing world were stunted, 180 million were underweight and

---

[11] These numbers are slightly lower than those reported in 1993 (de Onis *et al.*, 1993) because the WHO Global Database on Child Growth has since been updated, either by substituting more recent survey results for some countries or by including first-time survey results for others. In both estimates, 1990 population figures were used. It would not be correct to interpret these differences as necessarily indicating a worldwide reduction in the number of undernourished children.

almost 50 million were wasted. As in the case of food inadequacy, there is some evidence that the proportion of children who are undernourished has declined in the last two decades but the magnitude of the problem remains daunting. Estimates of the numbers of undernourished schoolchildren, adolescents and adults will have to await many additional data on a worldwide basis. The coexistence of undernutrition and obesity, although not yet a general phenomenon in the developing world, is likely to be increasingly prevalent in some population groups.

Admittedly, not all the undernutrition arising from anthropometric shortfalls can be attributed to food deprivation alone because inadequate food consumption interacts in a complex manner with other forms of deprivation, such as unhygienic environments or lack of access to health care, to produce a state of undernutrition. However, inadequate access to food is the most basic of deprivations and goes hand in hand with most other forms. Food inadequacy may thus be a good indicator of general deprivation in its various manifestations. The remainder of this chapter examines these associations.

First, the 98 developing countries covered in this survey were classified into three groups according to their prevalence of food inadequacy: high, medium or low. Countries in which the proportion of people with inadequate access to food lies above the mean for all the developing countries are classified in the "high" food inadequacy group; countries in which the proportion lies within 1 SD below the mean are classified in the medium food inadequacy group; and countries in which the proportion lies further below are considered as belonging to the low food inadequacy group.[12] Using the same procedure, i.e. by taking the mean and the mean -1 SD as the cutoff point for the classification, countries were classified into high, medium and low groups also in terms of per caput GDP (adjusted for parity of purchasing power), the human development index (HDI) published by the United Nations Development Programme (UNDP, 1995) and the prevalence of underweight children as reported in Chapter 3.

Figure 8 compares the degree of food deprivation (the proportion of the population with inadequate access to food) with the level of nutritional deprivation as measured by the proportion of underweight children among the population under five years of age. An association between the two clearly exists, although it is not perfect. Contrasting the highly deprived countries with those with low levels of food deprivation, the proportion of countries with a high prevalence of child weight deficiency declines (from 55 to 8 percent) while the proportion with a low prevalence

---

[12] There were 37 countries in the "high" food inadequacy group, 40 in the "medium" inadequacy group and 21 in the "low" inadequacy group.

of child weight deficiency increases (from 4 to 67 percent). The proportions of moderately food-deprived countries tend to fall in between. To some extent, therefore, food deprivation and poor nutritional status go together, but the exceptions are also quite significant. As can be seen from Figure 8 two out of five countries with a high degree of food deprivation had only a moderate prevalence of weight deficiency, while one in ten countries with a low degree of food deprivation had a high prevalence of weight deficiency.

The absence of a strong association between food deprivation and nutritional status is to be expected in view of the points made earlier about multiple determinants of nutritional status.[13] It is quite possible that, in some countries, despite a high prevalence of food inadequacy, a moderate improvement can still be made in nutritional status by acting on other determinants such as hygiene and health care while, in other countries, the poor provision of hygiene and health care maintained a low nutritional status despite low degrees of food inadequacy.

---

[13] An additional reason is that food inadequacy figures refer to the whole population, covering both adults and children, while the prevalence of weight deficiency refers only to the subpopulation of children under five years of age.

83

**FIGURE 8**

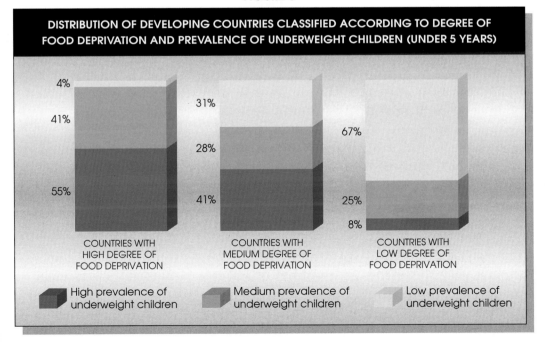

DISTRIBUTION OF DEVELOPING COUNTRIES CLASSIFIED ACCORDING TO DEGREE OF FOOD DEPRIVATION AND PREVALENCE OF UNDERWEIGHT CHILDREN (UNDER 5 YEARS)

But the observed association is much closer between food deprivation and indicators of general socio-economic development such as a low per caput GDP and a low HDI. Figure 9 shows the cross-country association between food deprivation and per caput GDP. As many as 89 percent of highly food-deprived countries belong to the low GDP group. It is not surprising that countries with the highest degree of food inadequacy are generally the poorest, but the exceptions are of some interest. One in ten countries in the high food inadequacy group is in the medium-income range, while one in ten countries in the low food inadequacy group is in the lowest income range. This shows that, while there is a close association between general levels of food adequacy and economic affluence across countries, it is sometimes possible to reduce food inadequacy substantially even at low levels of national income, just as it is possible to encounter countries with high degrees of food inadequacy at higher levels of national income. In other words, moderate increases in national income may not be a guarantee of corresponding reductions in food inadequacy, just as a low income need not be an insurmountable obstacle to improving the national level of food adequacy. One caveat should be borne in mind: this cross-country analysis does not establish cause and effect; rather, the associations merely suggest that these relationships are amenable to appropriate policy measures.

84

**FIGURE 9**

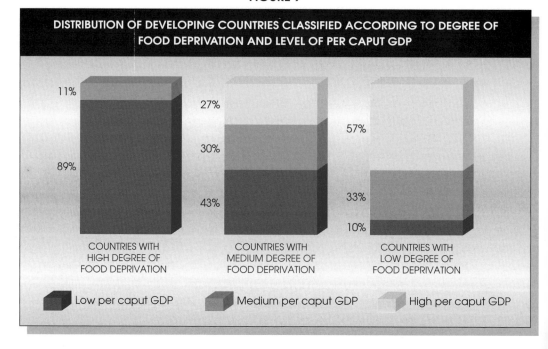

**DISTRIBUTION OF DEVELOPING COUNTRIES CLASSIFIED ACCORDING TO DEGREE OF FOOD DEPRIVATION AND LEVEL OF PER CAPUT GDP**

11%

27%

57%

30%

89%

43%

33%

10%

COUNTRIES WITH
HIGH DEGREE OF
FOOD DEPRIVATION

COUNTRIES WITH
MEDIUM DEGREE OF
FOOD DEPRIVATION

COUNTRIES WITH
LOW DEGREE OF
FOOD DEPRIVATION

Low per caput GDP      Medium per caput GDP      High per caput GDP

The HDI is a more comprehensive indicator of general welfare since, in addition to per caput GDP, it also considers the levels of literacy and life expectancy at birth. The association between this indicator and food deprivation is again found to be close (Figure 10). Nearly 80 percent of the countries with a high degree of food inadequacy are also characterized by low levels of HDI; on the other hand, among the countries with a low level of food inadequacy there is none with a low level of human development. Once again, it is useful to note the exceptions. One in five of the food-deprived countries are characterized by a medium HDI, which indicates that, unless appropriate measures are taken, high levels of food deprivation can persist even when the combination of overall economic development and improved access to education and health facilities has succeeded in bringing about a moderate improvement in general human welfare.

This brief discussion highlights two issues of policy interest: i) Although it is essential to reduce national food inadequacy to combat the problem of child undernutrition, there are other risk factors besides inadequate access to food. ii) While measures to eliminate general deprivation – as indicated by a low per caput GDP or HDI, for example, will often go a long way towards improving food access, there is no guarantee that they will. On the other hand, it may be possible to reduce

85

**FIGURE 10**

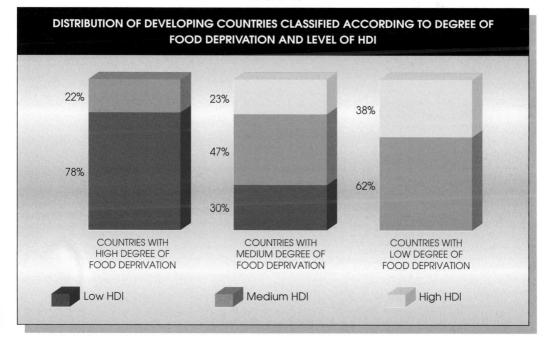

DISTRIBUTION OF DEVELOPING COUNTRIES CLASSIFIED ACCORDING TO DEGREE OF FOOD DEPRIVATION AND LEVEL OF HDI

22%

23%

38%

47%

78%

62%

30%

COUNTRIES WITH
HIGH DEGREE OF
FOOD DEPRIVATION

COUNTRIES WITH
MEDIUM DEGREE OF
FOOD DEPRIVATION

COUNTRIES WITH
LOW DEGREE OF
FOOD DEPRIVATION

Low HDI          Medium HDI          High HDI

food inadequacy substantially even when general socio-economic deprivation persists.

A more in-depth country-by-country analysis, which is beyond the scope of this survey, would provide greater insights into the relative effectiveness of food and non-food inputs to improve child nutritional status and the synergistic effects that exist between these inputs.

# Appendixes

•

**APPENDIX 1**

Country composition of regional
aggregates and economic groups

•

**APPENDIX 2**

Country data on food and
nutrition situation

•

**APPENDIX 3**

Methodology for assessing food
inadequacy in developing countries

•

**APPENDIX 4**

Anthropometric assessment
of nutritional status

**APPENDIX 1**

# Country composition of regional aggregates and economic groups

## DEVELOPED COUNTRIES

| Industrialized countries | | | Transition economies |
|---|---|---|---|
| Australia | Greece | Portugal | Albania |
| Austria | Ireland | South Africa | Bulgaria |
| Belgium/Luxembourg | Israel | Spain | Czechoslovakia |
| Canada | Italy | Sweden | Hungary |
| Denmark | Japan | Switzerland | Poland |
| Finland | Netherlands | United Kingdom | Romania |
| France | New Zealand | United States | USSR |
| Germany | Norway | | Yugoslavia, SFR |

## DEVELOPING COUNTRIES

| Near East and North Africa | MIC | LIC | LIFDC | LDC | East and Southeast Asia | MIC | LIC | LIFDC | LDC |
|---|---|---|---|---|---|---|---|---|---|
| Afghanistan | | * | * | * | Cambodia | | * | * | * |
| Algeria | * | | | | China | | * | * | |
| Egypt | | * | * | | Hong Kong [1] | | | | |
| Iran, Islamic Rep. | * | | | | Indonesia | * | | * | |
| Iraq | * | | | | Korea, Dem. People's Rep. | * | | | |
| Jordan | * | | * | | Korea, Rep. | * | | | |
| Kuwait [1] | | | | | Laos | | * | * | * |
| Lebanon | * | | | | Malaysia | * | | | |
| Libyan Arab Jam. | * | | | | Mongolia | | * | * | |
| Morocco | * | | * | | Myanmar | | * | | * |
| Saudi Arabia | * | | | | Philippines | * | | * | |
| Syrian Arab Republic | * | | * | | Thailand | * | | | |
| Tunisia | * | | | | Viet Nam | | * | | |
| Turkey | * | | | | | | | | |
| United Arab Emirates [1] | | | | | **South Asia** | | | | |
| Yemen | | * | * | * | | | | | |
| | | | | | Bangladesh | | * | * | * |
| | | | | | India | | * | * | |
| | | | | | Nepal | | * | * | * |
| | | | | | Pakistan | | * | * | |
| | | | | | Sri Lanka | | * | * | |

(continued)

*(continued)*

## DEVELOPING COUNTRIES

### Sub-Saharan Africa

| | MIC | LIC | LIFDC | LDC |
|---|---|---|---|---|
| Angola | * | | * | |
| Benin | | * | * | * |
| Botswana | * | | | |
| Burkina Faso | | * | * | * |
| Burundi | | * | * | * |
| Cameroon | * | | * | |
| Central African Rep. | | * | * | * |
| Chad | | * | * | * |
| Congo | * | | * | |
| Côte D'ivoire | | * | * | |
| Ethiopia, PDR | | * | * | * |
| Gabon | * | | | |
| Gambia | | * | * | * |
| Ghana | | * | * | |
| Guinea | | * | * | * |
| Kenya | | * | * | |
| Lesotho | | * | * | * |
| Liberia | | * | * | * |
| Madagascar | | * | * | * |
| Malawi | | * | * | * |
| Mali | | * | * | * |
| Mauritania | | * | * | * |
| Mauritius | * | | | |
| Mozambique | | * | * | * |
| Namibia | * | | | |
| Niger | | * | * | * |
| Nigeria | | * | * | |
| Rwanda | | * | * | * |
| Senegal | * | | * | |
| Sierra Leone | | * | * | * |
| Somalia | | * | * | * |
| Sudan | | * | * | * |
| Swaziland | * | | * | |
| Togo | | * | * | * |
| Uganda | | * | * | * |
| United Rep. of Tanzania | | * | * | * |
| Zaire | | * | * | * |
| Zambia | | * | * | * |
| Zimbabwe | | * | * | |

### Latin America and the Caribbean

| | MIC | LIC | LIFDC | LDC |
|---|---|---|---|---|
| Argentina | * | | | |
| Bolivia | * | | * | |
| Brazil | * | | | |
| Chile | * | | | |
| Colombia | * | | * | |
| Costa Rica | * | | | |
| Cuba | * | | | |
| Dominican Rep. | * | | * | |
| Ecuador | * | | * | |
| El Salvador | * | | * | |
| Guatemala | * | | * | |
| Guyana | | * | | |
| Haiti | | * | * | * |
| Honduras | | * | * | |
| Jamaica | * | | | |
| Mexico | * | | | |
| Nicaragua | | * | * | |
| Panama | * | | | |
| Paraguay | * | | | |
| Peru | * | | | |
| Suriname | * | | | |
| Trinidad and Tobago | * | | | |
| Uruguay | * | | | |
| Venezuela | * | | | |

### Other

| | MIC | LIC | LIFDC | LDC |
|---|---|---|---|---|
| Papua New Guinea | * | | * | |

[1] High-income country.
*Note:* MIC: Middle-income country.
LIC: Low-income country.
LIFDC: Low-income food-deficit country.
LDC: Least developed country.

**APPENDIX 2**

# Country data on food and nutrition situation

## FOOD SUPPLY
TABLE 1.  **Per caput dietary energy supply, 1969-71, 1979-81 and 1990-92**
TABLE 2.  **Per caput dietary protein and fat supply, 1969-71, 1979-81 and 1990-92**

## COMPOSITION OF FOOD SUPPLY
TABLE 3.  **Share of major food groups in total dietary energy supply, 1990-92**
TABLE 4.  **Share of major food groups in total dietary protein supply, 1990-92**
TABLE 5.  **Share of major food groups in total dietary fat supply, 1990-92**
TABLE 6.  **Share of main cereals and roots in total dietary energy supply, 1969-71 and 1990-92**

## FOOD INADEQUACY AND UNDERNUTRITION
TABLE 7.  **Relative inadequacy of food supply in developing countries, 1969-71, 1979-81 and 1990-92**
TABLE 8.  **Prevalence of undernutrition in children under five in developing countries**

## TABLE 1

| | Population 1990-92 | Per caput DES | | | |
|---|---|---|---|---|---|
| | | kcal/day | | | Annual growth rate |
| | | 1969-71 | 1979-81 | 1990-92 | 1969-71 to 1990-92 |
| | *(Millions)* | | | | *(Percentage)* |
| **WORLD** | 5 358.8 | 2 440 | 2 580 | 2 720 | 0.5 |
| **Africa** | 656.9 | 2 220 | 2 280 | 2 290 | 0.2 |
| Algeria | 25.6 | 1 830 | 2 620 | 2 900 | 2.2 |
| Angola | 9.5 | 2 110 | 2 160 | 1 840 | -0.7 |
| Benin | 4.8 | 2 160 | 2 190 | 2 520 | 0.7 |
| Botswana | 1.3 | 2 150 | 2 160 | 2 320 | 0.4 |
| Burkina Faso | 9.3 | 1 730 | 1 680 | 2 140 | 1.0 |
| Burundi | 5.7 | 2 100 | 2 040 | 1 950 | -0.4 |
| Cameroon | 11.9 | 2 320 | 2 350 | 2 040 | -0.6 |
| Central African Rep. | 3.1 | 2 360 | 2 270 | 1 720 | -1.5 |
| Chad | 5.7 | 2 170 | 1 680 | 1 810 | -0.9 |
| Congo | 2.3 | 2 060 | 2 220 | 2 210 | 0.3 |
| Côte d'Ivoire | 12.4 | 2 420 | 2 820 | 2 460 | 0.1 |
| Egypt | 53.6 | 2 510 | 3 130 | 3 340 | 1.4 |
| Ethiopia, PDR | 51.4 | 1 700 | 1 810 | 1 620 | -0.3 |
| Gabon | 1.2 | 2 180 | 2 400 | 2 490 | 0.6 |
| Gambia | 0.9 | 2 200 | 2 030 | 2 320 | 0.3 |
| Ghana | 15.5 | 2 200 | 1 910 | 2 090 | -0.3 |
| Guinea | 5.9 | 2 170 | 2 260 | 2 400 | 0.5 |
| Kenya | 24.4 | 2 200 | 2 150 | 1 970 | -0.5 |
| Lesotho | 1.8 | 2 000 | 2 260 | 2 260 | 0.6 |
| Liberia | 2.6 | 2 230 | 2 400 | 1 780 | -1.1 |
| Libyan Arab Jam. | 4.7 | 2 440 | 3 440 | 3 290 | 1.4 |
| Madagascar | 12.4 | 2 450 | 2 440 | 2 160 | -0.6 |
| Malawi | 10.0 | 2 360 | 2 280 | 1 910 | -1.0 |
| Mali | 9.5 | 2 050 | 1 800 | 2 230 | 0.4 |
| Mauritania | 2.1 | 1 940 | 2 110 | 2 610 | 1.4 |
| Mauritius | 1.1 | 2 320 | 2 670 | 2 780 | 0.9 |
| Morocco | 25.7 | 2 420 | 2 720 | 3 000 | 1.0 |
| Mozambique | 14.5 | 1 940 | 1 920 | 1 740 | -0.5 |
| Namibia | 1.5 | 2 180 | 2 210 | 2 190 | 0.0 |
| Niger | 8.0 | 1 990 | 2 240 | 2 190 | 0.5 |
| Nigeria | 112.1 | 2 380 | 1 960 | 2 100 | -0.6 |
| Rwanda | 7.3 | 2 040 | 2 090 | 1 860 | -0.4 |
| Senegal | 7.5 | 2 460 | 2 450 | 2 310 | -0.3 |
| Sierra Leone | 4.3 | 2 170 | 2 110 | 1 820 | -0.8 |
| Somalia | 7.7 | 1 810 | 1 870 | 1 590 | -0.6 |
| South Africa | 38.9 | 2 800 | 2 820 | 2 810 | 0.0 |
| Sudan | 25.9 | 2 190 | 2 260 | 2 150 | -0.1 |
| Swaziland | 0.8 | 2 310 | 2 480 | 2 680 | 0.7 |
| Togo | 3.6 | 2 300 | 2 240 | 2 290 | -0.0 |
| Tunisia | 8.2 | 2 280 | 2 810 | 3 260 | 1.7 |
| Uganda | 18.1 | 2 300 | 2 130 | 2 220 | -0.2 |
| United Rep. of Tanzania | 26.9 | 1 740 | 2 280 | 2 110 | 0.9 |
| Zaire | 38.6 | 2 160 | 2 070 | 2 090 | -0.1 |
| Zambia | 8.4 | 2 210 | 2 180 | 2 020 | -0.4 |
| Zimbabwe | 10.3 | 2 160 | 2 230 | 2 080 | -0.2 |
| **North and Central America** | 422.9 | 3 020 | 3 190 | 3 380 | 0.5 |
| Canada | 27.0 | 3 030 | 3 020 | 3 100 | 0.1 |
| Costa Rica | 3.1 | 2 410 | 2 630 | 2 870 | 0.8 |
| Cuba | 10.7 | 2 660 | 2 940 | 3 000 | 0.6 |
| Dominican Rep. | 7.3 | 2 020 | 2 270 | 2 270 | 0.6 |

*(continued)*

(continued)

TABLE 1

| | Population 1990-92 | Per caput DES | | | |
|---|---|---|---|---|---|
| | | kcal/day | | | Annual growth rate |
| | | 1969-71 | 1979-81 | 1990-92 | 1969-71 to 1990-92 |
| | (Millions) | | | | (Percentage) |

**PER CAPUT DIETARY ENERGY SUPPLY, 1969-71, 1979-81 AND 1990-92**

| | Population 1990-92 (Millions) | 1969-71 | 1979-81 | 1990-92 | Annual growth rate 1969-71 to 1990-92 (Percentage) |
|---|---|---|---|---|---|
| El Salvador | 5.2 | 1 860 | 2 320 | 2 530 | 1.5 |
| Guatemala | 9.5 | 2 080 | 2 230 | 2 280 | 0.4 |
| Haiti | 6.6 | 1 950 | 2 070 | 1 740 | -0.6 |
| Honduras | 5.3 | 2 140 | 2 090 | 2 310 | 0.4 |
| Jamaica | 2.4 | 2 520 | 2 640 | 2 580 | 0.1 |
| Mexico | 86.3 | 2 740 | 3 180 | 3 190 | 0.7 |
| Nicaragua | 3.8 | 2 360 | 2 320 | 2 290 | -0.2 |
| Panama | 2.5 | 2 300 | 2 280 | 2 240 | -0.1 |
| Trinidad and Tobago | 1.3 | 2 500 | 2 950 | 2 630 | 0.3 |
| United States | 251.8 | 3 230 | 3 360 | 3 700 | 0.6 |
| **South America** | **299.2** | **2 500** | **2 650** | **2 670** | **0.3** |
| Argentina | 32.7 | 3 280 | 3 200 | 2 950 | -0.5 |
| Bolivia | 7.3 | 1 950 | 2 060 | 2 030 | 0.2 |
| Brazil | 151.6 | 2 460 | 2 680 | 2 790 | 0.6 |
| Chile | 13.4 | 2 650 | 2 650 | 2 540 | -0.2 |
| Colombia | 32.9 | 2 060 | 2 460 | 2 630 | 1.2 |
| Ecuador | 10.8 | 2 140 | 2 320 | 2 540 | 0.8 |
| Guyana | 0.8 | 2 280 | 2 550 | 2 350 | 0.1 |
| Paraguay | 4.4 | 2 680 | 2 700 | 2 620 | -0.1 |
| Peru | 22.0 | 2 320 | 2 110 | 1 880 | -1.0 |
| Suriname | 0.4 | 2 240 | 2 450 | 2 510 | 0.6 |
| Uruguay | 3.1 | 2 970 | 2 830 | 2 680 | -0.5 |
| Venezuela | 19.7 | 2 370 | 2 730 | 2 590 | 0.4 |
| **Asia** | **3 162.7** | **2 110** | **2 310** | **2 560** | **0.9** |
| Afghanistan | 16.3 | 2 190 | 2 210 | 1 660 | -1.3 |
| Bangladesh | 116.5 | 2 120 | 1 910 | 1 990 | -0.3 |
| Cambodia | 8.6 | 2 480 | 1 770 | 2 100 | -0.8 |
| China | 1 170.9 | 2 010 | 2 350 | 2 710 | 1.4 |
| Hong Kong | 5.8 | 2 670 | 2 800 | 3 150 | 0.8 |
| India | 862.8 | 2 040 | 2 080 | 2 330 | 0.6 |
| Indonesia | 187.7 | 2 050 | 2 450 | 2 700 | 1.3 |
| Iran, Islamic Rep. | 59.9 | 2 080 | 2 650 | 2 760 | 1.4 |
| Iraq | 19.0 | 2 260 | 2 770 | 2 270 | 0.0 |
| Israel | 5.0 | 3 050 | 3 010 | 3 140 | 0.1 |
| Japan | 123.9 | 2 680 | 2 750 | 2 900 | 0.4 |
| Jordan | 3.4 | 2 440 | 2 670 | 2 900 | 0.8 |
| Korea, Dem. People's Rep. | 22.2 | 2 380 | 3 020 | 2 930 | 1.0 |
| Korea, Rep. | 43.8 | 2 820 | 3 120 | 3 270 | 0.7 |
| Kuwait | 1.2 | 2 640 | 3 000 | 2 460 | -0.3 |
| Laos | 4.3 | 2 150 | 2 360 | 2 210 | 0.1 |
| Lebanon | 2.8 | 2 330 | 2 710 | 3 260 | 1.6 |
| Malaysia | 18.3 | 2 470 | 2 700 | 2 830 | 0.7 |
| Mongolia | 2.3 | 2 250 | 2 400 | 2 100 | -0.3 |
| Myanmar | 42.7 | 2 060 | 2 320 | 2 580 | 1.1 |
| Nepal | 20.1 | 1 910 | 1 870 | 2 140 | 0.6 |
| Pakistan | 121.5 | 2 180 | 2 150 | 2 340 | 0.3 |
| Philippines | 63.8 | 1 770 | 2 200 | 2 290 | 1.2 |
| Saudi Arabia | 15.4 | 1 880 | 2 860 | 2 730 | 1.8 |
| Sri Lanka | 17.4 | 2 270 | 2 320 | 2 230 | -0.1 |
| Syrian Arab Rep. | 12.8 | 2 340 | 2 970 | 3 220 | 1.5 |
| Thailand | 55.4 | 2 190 | 2 220 | 2 380 | 0.4 |
| Turkey | 57.2 | 2 990 | 3 270 | 3 510 | 0.8 |

(continued)

*(continued)* **TABLE 1**

## PER CAPUT DIETARY ENERGY SUPPLY, 1969-71, 1979-81 AND 1990-92

| | Population 1990-92 | Per caput DES | | | |
|---|---|---|---|---|---|
| | | kcal/day | | | Annual growth rate |
| | | 1969-71 | 1979-81 | 1990-92 | 1969-71 to 1990-92 |
| | *(Millions)* | | | | *(Percentage)* |
| United Arab Emirates | 1.6 | 3 140 | 3 320 | 3 370 | 0.3 |
| Viet Nam | 68.1 | 2 190 | 2 100 | 2 200 | 0.0 |
| Yemen | 12.1 | 1 780 | 1 950 | 2 160 | 0.9 |
| **Europe** | **501.7** | **3 240** | **3 380** | **3 430** | **0.3** |
| Albania | 3.3 | 2 450 | 2 740 | 2 630 | 0.3 |
| Austria | 7.8 | 3 250 | 3 370 | 3 530 | 0.4 |
| Belgium/Luxembourg | 10.4 | 3 270 | 3 310 | 3 670 | 0.6 |
| Bulgaria | 9.0 | 3 500 | 3 620 | 3 160 | -0.5 |
| Czechoslovakia | 15.6 | 3 360 | 3 350 | 3 360 | 0.0 |
| Denmark | 5.2 | 3 220 | 3 460 | 3 620 | 0.6 |
| Finland | 5.0 | 3 150 | 3 050 | 3 030 | -0.2 |
| France | 57.0 | 3 350 | 3 470 | 3 640 | 0.4 |
| Germany | 79.9 | 3 210 | 3 370 | 3 410 | 0.3 |
| Greece | 10.1 | 3 170 | 3 430 | 3 770 | 0.8 |
| Hungary | 10.3 | 3 350 | 3 480 | 3 560 | 0.3 |
| Ireland | 3.5 | 3 440 | 3 620 | 3 790 | 0.5 |
| Italy | 57.8 | 3 380 | 3 560 | 3 540 | 0.2 |
| Netherlands | 15.1 | 3 020 | 3 050 | 3 170 | 0.2 |
| Norway | 4.3 | 3 050 | 3 350 | 3 230 | 0.3 |
| Poland | 38.2 | 3 470 | 3 580 | 3 340 | -0.2 |
| Portugal | 9.8 | 2 990 | 2 900 | 3 620 | 0.9 |
| Romania | 23.3 | 3 060 | 3 380 | 3 160 | 0.2 |
| Spain | 39.0 | 2 810 | 3 250 | 3 680 | 1.3 |
| Sweden | 8.6 | 2 900 | 3 020 | 2 960 | 0.1 |
| Switzerland | 6.8 | 3 510 | 3 540 | 3 380 | -0.2 |
| United Kingdom | 57.8 | 3 290 | 3 180 | 3 280 | -0.0 |
| Yugoslavia, SFR | 23.9 | 3 340 | 3 570 | 3 400 | 0.1 |
| **Oceania** | **24.7** | **3 070** | **3 020** | **3 140** | **0.1** |
| Australia | 17.3 | 3 200 | 3 080 | 3 180 | -0.0 |
| New Zealand | 3.4 | 3 260 | 3 350 | 3 580 | 0.4 |
| Papua New Guinea | 4.0 | 2 160 | 2 390 | 2 610 | 0.9 |
| **USSR** | **290.7** | **3 320** | **3 360** | **3 190** | **-0.2** |

**TABLE 2**

## PER CAPUT DIETARY PROTEIN AND FAT SUPPLY, 1969-71, 1979-81 AND 1990-92

| | Per caput dietary protein supply | | | | | | Per caput dietary fat supply | | | | | |
|---|---|---|---|---|---|---|---|---|---|---|---|---|
| | Total | | | Animal | | | Total | | | Animal | | |
| | 1969-71 | 1979-81 | 1990-92 | 1969-71 | 1979-81 | 1990-92 | 1969-71 | 1979-81 | 1990-92 | 1969-71 | 1979-81 | 1990-92 |
| | | | | | | *(g/day)* | | | | | | |
| **WORLD** | 65 | 68 | 71 | 22 | 23 | 25 | 55 | 61 | 69 | 28 | 30 | 32 |
| **Africa** | 57 | 57 | 57 | 12 | 13 | 12 | 44 | 48 | 47 | 11 | 12 | 11 |
| Algeria | 48 | 67 | 77 | 9 | 14 | 20 | 36 | 59 | 69 | 12 | 17 | 21 |
| Angola | 45 | 52 | 41 | 13 | 17 | 14 | 34 | 51 | 44 | 9 | 12 | 12 |
| Benin | 50 | 52 | 59 | 10 | 10 | 10 | 44 | 49 | 50 | 5 | 6 | 6 |
| Botswana | 76 | 72 | 69 | 27 | 26 | 29 | 45 | 50 | 67 | 26 | 25 | 37 |
| Burkina Faso | 53 | 50 | 63 | 7 | 7 | 7 | 30 | 32 | 43 | 6 | 5 | 7 |
| Burundi | 73 | 68 | 62 | 5 | 5 | 4 | 15 | 16 | 14 | 4 | 4 | 4 |
| Cameroon | 60 | 59 | 49 | 11 | 12 | 12 | 46 | 49 | 44 | 6 | 8 | 8 |
| Central African Rep. | 36 | 34 | 37 | 8 | 10 | 13 | 55 | 65 | 55 | 6 | 9 | 12 |
| Chad | 70 | 55 | 55 | 13 | 14 | 15 | 49 | 39 | 44 | 9 | 9 | 9 |
| Congo | 36 | 41 | 48 | 13 | 16 | 20 | 44 | 47 | 56 | 6 | 6 | 11 |
| Côte d'Ivoire | 52 | 60 | 51 | 14 | 16 | 12 | 41 | 52 | 46 | 9 | 10 | 6 |
| Egypt | 68 | 78 | 87 | 9 | 12 | 13 | 50 | 70 | 65 | 13 | 19 | 17 |
| Ethiopia, PDR | 58 | 60 | 51 | 11 | 9 | 8 | 28 | 25 | 25 | 10 | 8 | 7 |
| Gabon | 60 | 65 | 63 | 33 | 35 | 28 | 38 | 42 | 50 | 13 | 16 | 17 |
| Gambia | 55 | 48 | 56 | 11 | 11 | 12 | 57 | 51 | 53 | 7 | 7 | 7 |
| Ghana | 49 | 43 | 45 | 16 | 14 | 14 | 37 | 35 | 35 | 6 | 5 | 5 |
| Guinea | 47 | 51 | 53 | 4 | 6 | 7 | 55 | 52 | 48 | 3 | 5 | 4 |
| Kenya | 64 | 57 | 52 | 15 | 15 | 17 | 35 | 42 | 46 | 15 | 15 | 17 |
| Lesotho | 60 | 66 | 65 | 10 | 12 | 10 | 24 | 32 | 35 | 8 | 10 | 10 |
| Liberia | 42 | 47 | 34 | 11 | 11 | 8 | 41 | 46 | 40 | 6 | 5 | 4 |
| Libyan Arab Jam. | 59 | 89 | 79 | 20 | 35 | 26 | 72 | 112 | 111 | 24 | 43 | 26 |
| Madagascar | 61 | 59 | 51 | 18 | 18 | 15 | 34 | 37 | 32 | 18 | 18 | 16 |
| Malawi | 73 | 66 | 54 | 7 | 6 | 5 | 44 | 40 | 24 | 7 | 7 | 4 |
| Mali | 62 | 55 | 62 | 19 | 18 | 15 | 43 | 39 | 43 | 16 | 14 | 12· |
| Mauritania | 76 | 73 | 80 | 42 | 36 | 33 | 52 | 58 | 60 | 38 | 35 | 31 |
| Mauritius | 49 | 61 | 68 | 13 | 23 | 28 | 50 | 67 | 75 | 10 | 18 | 25 |
| Morocco | 64 | 71 | 83 | 10 | 12 | 14 | 42 | 52 | 57 | 14 | 13 | 15 |
| Mozambique | 36 | 32 | 32 | 5 | 4 | 4 | 28 | 32 | 37 | 5 | 4 | 4 |
| Namibia | 65 | 66 | 62 | 26 | 26 | 20 | 44 | 41 | 34 | 26 | 23 | 17 |
| Niger | 55 | 64 | 59 | 14 | 13 | 9 | 31 | 36 | 31 | 12 | 11 | 8 |
| Nigeria | 54 | 43 | 44 | 6 | 9 | 5 | 52 | 49 | 49 | 4 | 5 | 4 |
| Rwanda | 56 | 52 | 46 | 3 | 4 | 3 | 12 | 14 | 16 | 2 | 4 | 3 |
| Senegal | 66 | 69 | 66 | 17 | 16 | 18 | 68 | 65 | 60 | 12 | 9 | 11 |
| Sierra Leone | 44 | 46 | 38 | 8 | 11 | 7 | 64 | 58 | 56 | 4 | 4 | 3 |
| Somalia | 62 | 61 | 49 | 37 | 37 | 23 | 65 | 72 | 50 | 46 | 43 | 29 |
| South Africa | 73 | 74 | 71 | 27 | 27 | 25 | 68 | 67 | 69 | 34 | 30 | 27 |
| Sudan | 62 | 64 | 63 | 19 | 25 | 22 | 67 | 81 | 62 | 22 | 30 | 26 |
| Swaziland | 66 | 66 | 66 | 20 | 22 | 20 | 43 | 46 | 53 | 21 | 23 | 20 |
| Togo | 50 | 48 | 53 | 7 | 7 | 9 | 33 | 40 | 46 | 4 | 4 | 7 |
| Tunisia | 60 | 77 | 87 | 11 | 16 | 18 | 57 | 69 | 89 | 11 | 15 | 17 |
| Uganda | 56 | 48 | 52 | 12 | 11 | 11 | 35 | 21 | 28 | 8 | 9 | 10 |
| United Rep. of Tanzania | 42 | 56 | 51 | 11 | 11 | 12 | 27 | 31 | 31 | 10 | 9 | 9 |
| Zaire | 37 | 34 | 33 | 9 | 7 | 6 | 35 | 34 | 34 | 4 | 3 | 3 |
| Zambia | 64 | 58 | 52 | 15 | 11 | 9 | 41 | 36 | 28 | 10 | 8 | 6 |
| Zimbabwe | 60 | 59 | 53 | 11 | 12 | 10 | 49 | 54 | 52 | 14 | 15 | 14 |
| **North and Central America** | 90 | 92 | 97 | 54 | 54 | 55 | 113 | 121 | 128 | 66 | 65 | 63 |
| Canada | 93 | 92 | 97 | 60 | 58 | 58 | 125 | 131 | 133 | 91 | 84 | 73 |
| Costa Rica | 57 | 65 | 69 | 24 | 32 | 33 | 57 | 66 | 78 | 24 | 31 | 32 |

*(continued)*

(continued)

## TABLE 2

### PER CAPUT DIETARY PROTEIN AND FAT SUPPLY, 1969-71, 1979-81 AND 1990-92

| | Per caput dietary protein supply | | | | | | Per caput dietary fat supply | | | | | |
|---|---|---|---|---|---|---|---|---|---|---|---|---|
| | Total | | | Animal | | | Total | | | Animal | | |
| | 1969-71 | 1979-81 | 1990-92 | 1969-71 | 1979-81 | 1990-92 | 1969-71 | 1979-81 | 1990-92 | 1969-71 | 1979-81 | 1990-92 |
| | | | | | | (g/day) | | | | | | |
| Cuba | 67 | 71 | 66 | 34 | 35 | 32 | 69 | 78 | 77 | 45 | 54 | 40 |
| Dominican Rep. | 44 | 49 | 50 | 16 | 19 | 21 | 48 | 57 | 65 | 15 | 19 | 19 |
| El Salvador | 47 | 57 | 62 | 12 | 15 | 14 | 39 | 50 | 58 | 13 | 19 | 18 |
| Guatemala | 56 | 56 | 57 | 12 | 10 | 11 | 38 | 43 | 42 | 13 | 11 | 11 |
| Haiti | 45 | 49 | 41 | 7 | 8 | 7 | 27 | 35 | 26 | 9 | 8 | 6 |
| Honduras | 54 | 51 | 56 | 14 | 15 | 15 | 41 | 42 | 61 | 18 | 18 | 19 |
| Jamaica | 66 | 63 | 64 | 30 | 27 | 29 | 60 | 64 | 64 | 27 | 24 | 25 |
| Mexico | 70 | 84 | 80 | 19 | 30 | 30 | 61 | 84 | 94 | 26 | 41 | 39 |
| Nicaragua | 70 | 62 | 55 | 27 | 21 | 14 | 49 | 49 | 52 | 31 | 23 | 16 |
| Panama | 58 | 57 | 59 | 26 | 32 | 30 | 51 | 68 | 65 | 29 | 30 | 32 |
| Trinidad and Tobago | 64 | 78 | 63 | 26 | 35 | 26 | 62 | 73 | 72 | 25 | 35 | 30 |
| United States | 101 | 101 | 112 | 69 | 68 | 72 | 137 | 145 | 154 | 81 | 78 | 79 |
| **South America** | **65** | **65** | **66** | **27** | **29** | **31** | **58** | **69** | **77** | **32** | **34** | **35** |
| Argentina | 104 | 107 | 97 | 66 | 72 | 64 | 112 | 116 | 103 | 70 | 75 | 67 |
| Bolivia | 48 | 53 | 52 | 15 | 20 | 19 | 42 | 51 | 51 | 30 | 36 | 27 |
| Brazil | 61 | 60 | 64 | 20 | 22 | 27 | 51 | 68 | 82 | 26 | 29 | 34 |
| Chile | 69 | 71 | 70 | 25 | 26 | 31 | 59 | 59 | 65 | 34 | 30 | 33 |
| Colombia | 48 | 53 | 59 | 22 | 23 | 27 | 42 | 50 | 62 | 23 | 25 | 29 |
| Ecuador | 50 | 49 | 52 | 18 | 21 | 22 | 50 | 59 | 90 | 23 | 24 | 26 |
| Guyana | 57 | 65 | 64 | 25 | 29 | 27 | 48 | 53 | 37 | 21 | 21 | 18 |
| Paraguay | 72 | 75 | 68 | 33 | 33 | 34 | 72 | 81 | 92 | 43 | 44 | 45 |
| Peru | 61 | 55 | 50 | 20 | 20 | 20 | 40 | 38 | 34 | 20 | 15 | 15 |
| Suriname | 57 | 61 | 63 | 25 | 28 | 26 | 45 | 52 | 58 | 17 | 21 | 22 |
| Uruguay | 91 | 85 | 83 | 59 | 53 | 51 | 112 | 103 | 96 | 94 | 79 | 75 |
| Venezuela | 60 | 70 | 65 | 26 | 35 | 29 | 54 | 78 | 75 | 22 | 29 | 24 |
| **Asia** | **52** | **57** | **64** | **9** | **11** | **15** | **29** | **36** | **50** | **11** | **14** | **20** |
| Afghanistan | 63 | 62 | 47 | 12 | 12 | 10 | 33 | 38 | 30 | 16 | 16 | 13 |
| Bangladesh | 45 | 42 | 43 | 6 | 5 | 5 | 15 | 14 | 17 | 4 | 3 | 3 |
| Cambodia | 58 | 41 | 51 | 8 | 5 | 9 | 22 | 13 | 20 | 8 | 3 | 8 |
| China | 49 | 56 | 67 | 6 | 8 | 15 | 23 | 32 | 52 | 10 | 15 | 29 |
| Hong Kong | 80 | 86 | 93 | 43 | 51 | 59 | 91 | 105 | 139 | 48 | 53 | 68 |
| India | 51 | 51 | 57 | 6 | 7 | 9 | 30 | 33 | 41 | 7 | 8 | 11 |
| Indonesia | 42 | 51 | 60 | 5 | 7 | 9 | 29 | 38 | 51 | 3 | 4 | 7 |
| Iran, Islamic Rep. | 55 | 69 | 72 | 13 | 17 | 16 | 43 | 61 | 63 | 17 | 23 | 18 |
| Iraq | 61 | 73 | 56 | 14 | 17 | 9 | 42 | 57 | 43 | 16 | 17 | 10 |
| Israel | 98 | 101 | 102 | 47 | 53 | 52 | 102 | 107 | 119 | 40 | 41 | 40 |
| Japan | 82 | 87 | 97 | 36 | 45 | 55 | 53 | 68 | 80 | 25 | 32 | 37 |
| Jordan | 67 | 68 | 77 | 16 | 20 | 24 | 59 | 64 | 80 | 16 | 22 | 26 |
| Korea, Dem. People's Rep. | 70 | 85 | 86 | 11 | 15 | 19 | 30 | 37 | 41 | 8 | 12 | 15 |
| Korea, Rep. | 72 | 82 | 85 | 9 | 18 | 32 | 25 | 41 | 69 | 9 | 19 | 30 |
| Kuwait | 76 | 91 | 69 | 33 | 49 | 35 | 72 | 92 | 88 | 34 | 50 | 39 |
| Laos | 58 | 64 | 61 | 11 | 14 | 14 | 27 | 34 | 34 | 14 | 19 | 20 |
| Lebanon | 59 | 75 | 86 | 19 | 28 | 27 | 61 | 80 | 98 | 24 | 35 | 36 |
| Malaysia | 50 | 57 | 58 | 17 | 25 | 28 | 55 | 78 | 100 | 19 | 26 | 31 |
| Mongolia | 82 | 82 | 73 | 55 | 52 | 49 | 87 | 85 | 78 | 80 | 78 | 71 |
| Myanmar | 53 | 60 | 64 | 8 | 8 | 8 | 33 | 35 | 43 | 6 | 7 | 7 |
| Nepal | 50 | 49 | 55 | 7 | 7 | 7 | 25 | 26 | 29 | 9 | 9 | 9 |
| Pakistan | 55 | 52 | 57 | 13 | 14 | 17 | 34 | 44 | 61 | 18 | 18 | 23 |
| Philippines | 44 | 51 | 53 | 20 | 21 | 22 | 33 | 35 | 38 | 18 | 16 | 19 |
| Saudi Arabia | 49 | 76 | 77 | 10 | 31 | 34 | 32 | 76 | 89 | 11 | 29 | 32 |

(continued)

(continued)

## TABLE 2

### PER CAPUT DIETARY PROTEIN AND FAT SUPPLY, 1969-71, 1979-81 AND 1990-92

| | Per caput dietary protein supply | | | | | | Per caput dietary fat supply | | | | | |
|---|---|---|---|---|---|---|---|---|---|---|---|---|
| | Total | | | Animal | | | Total | | | Animal | | |
| | 1969-71 | 1979-81 | 1990-92 | 1969-71 | 1979-81 | 1990-92 | 1969-71 | 1979-81 | 1990-92 | 1969-71 | 1979-81 | 1990-92 |
| | | | | | | (g/day) | | | | | | |
| Sri Lanka | 46 | 46 | 46 | 9 | 9 | 9 | 48 | 46 | 44 | 6 | 6 | 6 |
| Syrian Arab Rep. | 63 | 80 | 84 | 13 | 21 | 19 | 62 | 86 | 94 | 22 | 37 | 29 |
| Thailand | 51 | 49 | 53 | 17 | 15 | 19 | 30 | 32 | 44 | 14 | 14 | 16 |
| Turkey | 90 | 97 | 101 | 25 | 27 | 25 | 71 | 79 | 93 | 29 | 29 | 26 |
| United Arab Emirates | 85 | 103 | 108 | 42 | 57 | 55 | 86 | 120 | 112 | 76 | 66 | 61 |
| Viet Nam | 51 | 48 | 51 | 10 | 8 | 11 | 22 | 19 | 28 | 11 | 9 | 15 |
| Yemen | 50 | 59 | 58 | 6 | 13 | 11 | 30 | 36 | 40 | 12 | 14 | 9 |
| **Europe** | **93** | **100** | **100** | **49** | **57** | **58** | **119** | **134** | **142** | **77** | **86** | **87** |
| Albania | 71 | 81 | 82 | 18 | 22 | 25 | 50 | 60 | 62 | 29 | 28 | 34 |
| Austria | 89 | 94 | 101 | 51 | 60 | 64 | 130 | 152 | 164 | 88 | 100 | 100 |
| Belgium/Luxembourg | 93 | 99 | 104 | 54 | 62 | 65 | 138 | 146 | 172 | 89 | 98 | 111 |
| Bulgaria | 96 | 104 | 95 | 30 | 44 | 44 | 85 | 107 | 109 | 40 | 57 | 61 |
| Czechoslovakia | 95 | 99 | 95 | 51 | 58 | 52 | 113 | 122 | 123 | 80 | 88 | 84 |
| Denmark | 78 | 85 | 99 | 47 | 53 | 64 | 151 | 176 | 179 | 113 | 138 | 144 |
| Finland | 90 | 94 | 95 | 55 | 61 | 61 | 127 | 131 | 124 | 103 | 105 | 95 |
| France | 103 | 112 | 116 | 65 | 75 | 78 | 135 | 157 | 173 | 101 | 113 | 117 |
| Germany | 91 | 97 | 100 | 55 | 61 | 65 | 132 | 140 | 144 | 91 | 97 | 95 |
| Greece | 99 | 106 | 114 | 43 | 53 | 58 | 115 | 137 | 161 | 45 | 60 | 69 |
| Hungary | 93 | 98 | 95 | 41 | 49 | 50 | 116 | 135 | 154 | 99 | 108 | 113 |
| Ireland | 105 | 113 | 121 | 64 | 72 | 77 | 124 | 143 | 149 | 95 | 104 | 93 |
| Italy | 96 | 106 | 108 | 41 | 53 | 58 | 109 | 129 | 148 | 46 | 61 | 67 |
| Netherlands | 87 | 93 | 91 | 55 | 61 | 59 | 131 | 130 | 134 | 70 | 77 | 73 |
| Norway | 87 | 102 | 98 | 53 | 65 | 59 | 135 | 148 | 136 | 90 | 97 | 84 |
| Poland | 102 | 110 | 101 | 52 | 61 | 53 | 109 | 123 | 118 | 88 | 98 | 91 |
| Portugal | 81 | 76 | 102 | 34 | 36 | 53 | 82 | 97 | 137 | 34 | 45 | 70 |
| Romania | 89 | 103 | 95 | 28 | 46 | 43 | 71 | 99 | 95 | 39 | 59 | 58 |
| Spain | 82 | 95 | 104 | 39 | 53 | 61 | 100 | 137 | 182 | 46 | 69 | 93 |
| Sweden | 88 | 97 | 96 | 58 | 67 | 64 | 120 | 128 | 124 | 69 | 79 | 77 |
| Switzerland | 89 | 96 | 94 | 53 | 61 | 60 | 154 | 167 | 160 | 99 | 114 | 106 |
| United Kingdom | 91 | 88 | 92 | 55 | 52 | 53 | 147 | 140 | 144 | 108 | 97 | 85 |
| Yugoslavia, SFR | 93 | 102 | 65 | 27 | 38 | 26 | 86 | 106 | 73 | 52 | 69 | 44 |
| **Oceania** | **92** | **92** | **96** | **60** | **62** | **62** | **114** | **114** | **124** | **93** | **82** | **79** |
| Australia | 100 | 98 | 101 | 66 | 69 | 69 | 123 | 122 | 132 | 100 | 86 | 85 |
| New Zealand | 99 | 106 | 118 | 68 | 75 | 80 | 141 | 147 | 153 | 127 | 125 | 115 |
| Papua New Guinea | 42 | 48 | 50 | 15 | 17 | 17 | 33 | 42 | 62 | 16 | 18 | 20 |
| **USSR** | **102** | **103** | **104** | **46** | **51** | **53** | **85** | **95** | **94** | **59** | **64** | **64** |

TABLE 3

## SHARE OF MAJOR FOOD GROUPS IN TOTAL DIETARY ENERGY SUPPLY, 1990-92

| | Share in total DES | | | | | | | | |
|---|---|---|---|---|---|---|---|---|---|
| | Vegetable products | | | | | | Animal products | | |
| | Cereals | Sugar | Vegetable oils | Roots and tubers | Pulses and nuts | Others | Meat and offal | Milk | Others |
| | *(Percentage)* | | | | | | | | |
| **WORLD** | 51.2 | 8.8 | 8.2 | 5.0 | 4.0 | 7.1 | 7.4 | 4.3 | 4.0 |
| **Africa** | 49.4 | 6.3 | 8.5 | 14.9 | 5.8 | 7.7 | 3.2 | 2.5 | 1.7 |
| Algeria | 56.0 | 11.2 | 12.6 | 2.2 | 2.0 | 4.7 | 3.0 | 5.8 | 2.5 |
| Angola | 31.5 | 7.0 | 12.1 | 29.8 | 4.2 | 5.5 | 4.8 | 2.4 | 2.8 |
| Benin | 35.3 | 1.8 | 7.4 | 38.2 | 8.9 | 4.4 | 2.4 | 0.5 | 1.4 |
| Botswana | 44.7 | 11.8 | 6.9 | 1.5 | 4.4 | 7.5 | 7.3 | 9.4 | 6.5 |
| Burkina Faso | 75.6 | 1.7 | 4.0 | 0.9 | 8.7 | 4.2 | 2.7 | 1.4 | 0.8 |
| Burundi | 19.8 | 1.8 | 1.1 | 28.4 | 28.4 | 17.7 | 1.4 | 0.7 | 0.7 |
| Cameroon | 38.7 | 4.7 | 8.5 | 18.0 | 7.3 | 16.2 | 3.7 | 1.5 | 1.4 |
| Central African Rep. | 19.1 | 2.7 | 13.6 | 36.0 | 10.4 | 8.2 | 6.8 | 1.6 | 1.6 |
| Chad | 51.3 | 4.5 | 5.3 | 15.2 | 12.7 | 2.9 | 4.3 | 2.7 | 1.1 |
| Congo | 22.3 | 4.6 | 11.7 | 38.1 | 6.2 | 8.7 | 4.6 | 0.6 | 3.3 |
| Côte d'Ivoire | 36.9 | 4.9 | 8.8 | 27.2 | 5.3 | 12.2 | 2.4 | 0.8 | 1.5 |
| Egypt | 64.4 | 10.2 | 7.5 | 1.7 | 3.2 | 6.6 | 2.4 | 1.4 | 2.5 |
| Ethiopia, PDR | 70.8 | 2.1 | 3.0 | 4.2 | 10.4 | 2.8 | 3.6 | 2.0 | 1.1 |
| Gabon | 25.9 | 6.3 | 6.4 | 21.9 | 4.7 | 22.9 | 7.2 | 1.8 | 2.8 |
| Gambia | 64.9 | 8.6 | 11.4 | 1.0 | 6.1 | 2.4 | 2.8 | 1.3 | 1.5 |
| Ghana | 29.9 | 3.4 | 7.5 | 40.7 | 3.5 | 9.7 | 2.1 | 0.3 | 2.9 |
| Guinea | 47.9 | 4.2 | 11.9 | 13.9 | 4.9 | 14.0 | 1.3 | 1.0 | 1.0 |
| Kenya | 49.8 | 11.3 | 8.3 | 8.0 | 3.7 | 5.3 | 4.2 | 7.8 | 1.6 |
| Lesotho | 77.8 | 6.5 | 3.1 | 0.7 | 2.8 | 2.8 | 4.2 | 1.2 | 0.7 |
| Liberia | 44.9 | 2.5 | 14.6 | 22.3 | 3.3 | 8.2 | 2.2 | 0.2 | 1.8 |
| Libyan Arab Jam. | 45.2 | 11.2 | 18.1 | 1.7 | 3.8 | 7.5 | 4.4 | 6.0 | 2.1 |
| Madagascar | 54.6 | 3.4 | 3.2 | 21.0 | 2.1 | 5.1 | 6.2 | 3.0 | 1.5 |
| Malawi | 69.8 | 7.2 | 1.7 | 3.8 | 9.0 | 5.5 | 1.3 | 0.4 | 1.2 |
| Mali | 72.9 | 4.0 | 6.8 | 1.9 | 4.0 | 1.5 | 3.7 | 4.2 | 1.1 |
| Mauritania | 55.3 | 12.4 | 7.1 | 0.5 | 4.4 | 1.5 | 5.7 | 11.0 | 2.1 |
| Mauritius | 45.1 | 16.8 | 13.9 | 1.3 | 3.9 | 4.6 | 5.0 | 6.4 | 3.0 |
| Morocco | 63.1 | 10.2 | 8.1 | 1.9 | 4.1 | 5.5 | 2.8 | 1.5 | 2.7 |
| Mozambique | 36.2 | 1.9 | 12.3 | 39.5 | 4.9 | 2.0 | 1.9 | 0.6 | 0.7 |
| Namibia | 49.2 | 14.5 | 2.9 | 15.6 | 3.8 | 2.0 | 6.7 | 3.1 | 2.1 |
| Niger | 74.4 | 2.4 | 2.9 | 3.6 | 9.0 | 2.2 | 2.7 | 2.0 | 0.9 |
| Nigeria | 38.0 | 2.6 | 13.1 | 26.0 | 7.9 | 9.4 | 1.7 | 0.3 | 1.0 |
| Rwanda | 19.5 | 1.1 | 2.4 | 28.2 | 16.9 | 29.1 | 1.1 | 1.4 | 0.2 |
| Senegal | 63.6 | 7.2 | 12.1 | 1.0 | 5.2 | 2.1 | 3.6 | 2.5 | 2.6 |
| Sierra Leone | 53.5 | 2.6 | 21.6 | 4.4 | 7.3 | 7.2 | 1.1 | 0.6 | 1.7 |
| Somalia | 55.1 | 5.0 | 5.2 | 0.9 | 2.6 | 2.6 | 5.7 | 21.0 | 1.9 |
| South Africa | 53.7 | 12.9 | 9.3 | 1.7 | 1.1 | 7.8 | 8.2 | 3.4 | 1.9 |
| Sudan | 58.6 | 8.6 | 8.1 | 0.6 | 2.4 | 4.0 | 4.6 | 11.9 | 1.2 |
| Swaziland | 51.4 | 20.8 | 7.0 | 1.4 | 3.2 | 5.3 | 6.0 | 3.8 | 1.1 |
| Togo | 47.8 | 2.1 | 8.4 | 28.8 | 5.1 | 3.2 | 2.4 | 0.6 | 1.7 |
| Tunisia | 55.0 | 9.0 | 15.7 | 1.4 | 4.0 | 6.7 | 2.6 | 3.7 | 2.0 |
| Uganda | 18.6 | 1.7 | 1.6 | 27.8 | 14.7 | 28.9 | 3.1 | 1.8 | 1.8 |
| United Rep. of Tanzania | 45.6 | 2.4 | 4.8 | 24.6 | 6.6 | 9.1 | 2.7 | 1.8 | 2.3 |
| Zaire | 15.5 | 1.4 | 6.8 | 56.2 | 7.7 | 9.7 | 1.9 | 0.1 | 0.8 |
| Zambia | 70.3 | 7.6 | 2.3 | 9.9 | 1.7 | 3.3 | 2.7 | 0.7 | 1.5 |
| Zimbabwe | 59.0 | 11.7 | 7.7 | 1.6 | 7.1 | 3.7 | 3.0 | 3.4 | 2.7 |
| **North and Central America** | 28.7 | 16.5 | 13.4 | 2.4 | 3.8 | 9.5 | 12.5 | 8.4 | 4.8 |
| Canada | 21.8 | 14.0 | 13.8 | 3.4 | 4.5 | 11.3 | 14.8 | 9.2 | 7.3 |

*(continued)*

*(continued)*

**TABLE 3**

| SHARE OF MAJOR FOOD GROUPS IN TOTAL DIETARY ENERGY SUPPLY, 1990-92 | | | | | | | | | |
|---|---|---|---|---|---|---|---|---|---|
| | | | | | | | Share in total DES | | |
| | | | Vegetable products | | | | Animal products | | |
| | Cereals | Sugar | Vegetable oils | Roots and tubers | Pulses and nuts | Others | Meat and offal | Milk | Others |
| | | | | | *(Percentage)* | | | | |
| Costa Rica | 33.4 | 21.4 | 11.6 | 1.9 | 4.4 | 10.0 | 6.8 | 7.6 | 2.8 |
| Cuba | 31.9 | 25.5 | 9.2 | 4.8 | 4.1 | 5.5 | 6.5 | 5.8 | 6.6 |
| Dominican Rep. | 31.0 | 15.0 | 14.8 | 3.5 | 4.9 | 17.4 | 6.1 | 4.7 | 2.7 |
| El Salvador | 56.2 | 14.0 | 6.4 | 0.9 | 6.6 | 5.6 | 2.1 | 4.7 | 3.4 |
| Guatemala | 60.0 | 17.6 | 5.3 | 0.4 | 5.9 | 3.8 | 2.2 | 2.8 | 1.9 |
| Haiti | 40.7 | 14.5 | 3.0 | 10.9 | 11.2 | 14.1 | 2.8 | 1.6 | 1.0 |
| Honduras | 49.5 | 14.6 | 10.4 | 0.4 | 6.0 | 7.7 | 2.5 | 5.1 | 3.8 |
| Jamaica | 34.4 | 19.0 | 9.4 | 8.4 | 3.4 | 9.3 | 6.9 | 4.5 | 4.9 |
| Mexico | 46.1 | 15.0 | 10.3 | 0.8 | 5.4 | 6.1 | 7.7 | 4.5 | 4.1 |
| Nicaragua | 47.5 | 18.0 | 8.9 | 1.5 | 8.9 | 5.2 | 3.4 | 3.9 | 2.8 |
| Panama | 38.8 | 12.8 | 10.6 | 2.3 | 3.5 | 11.3 | 8.9 | 6.4 | 5.3 |
| Trinidad and Tobago | 39.3 | 18.3 | 11.2 | 2.3 | 5.5 | 7.4 | 5.6 | 5.4 | 4.9 |
| United States | 22.1 | 16.9 | 15.0 | 2.7 | 2.9 | 10.5 | 14.9 | 10.1 | 5.0 |
| **South America** | **35.0** | **16.3** | **11.7** | **5.4** | **4.4** | **8.6** | **9.3** | **5.8** | **3.3** |
| Argentina | 30.8 | 13.0 | 9.2 | 4.0 | 0.9 | 9.8 | 19.2 | 8.8 | 4.3 |
| Bolivia | 40.0 | 12.8 | 6.8 | 10.3 | 3.6 | 9.9 | 9.7 | 1.6 | 5.2 |
| Brazil | 34.4 | 16.8 | 13.2 | 5.3 | 6.3 | 7.3 | 8.0 | 5.5 | 3.1 |
| Chile | 43.1 | 15.1 | 8.9 | 4.2 | 1.5 | 8.4 | 9.1 | 5.9 | 3.8 |
| Colombia | 32.5 | 21.8 | 8.3 | 7.3 | 3.1 | 10.8 | 7.5 | 6.2 | 2.4 |
| Ecuador | 37.8 | 14.8 | 19.7 | 2.9 | 1.6 | 8.9 | 5.5 | 4.9 | 3.9 |
| Guyana | 53.0 | 13.9 | 3.4 | 2.3 | 5.3 | 9.3 | 5.2 | 2.9 | 4.6 |
| Paraguay | 24.0 | 9.2 | 12.8 | 15.7 | 4.6 | 11.4 | 14.4 | 3.7 | 4.1 |
| Peru | 43.2 | 16.7 | 6.0 | 7.9 | 2.8 | 10.4 | 6.0 | 3.5 | 3.5 |
| Suriname | 51.1 | 11.2 | 10.1 | 2.0 | 2.9 | 8.4 | 7.1 | 5.0 | 2.3 |
| Uruguay | 34.3 | 10.4 | 5.4 | 4.4 | 1.5 | 8.5 | 21.8 | 8.7 | 4.9 |
| Venezuela | 38.1 | 14.6 | 15.2 | 2.6 | 3.0 | 11.8 | 6.4 | 5.4 | 3.0 |
| **Asia** | **63.8** | **6.3** | **6.3** | **3.6** | **4.5** | **5.3** | **5.2** | **2.3** | **2.8** |
| Afghanistan | 76.3 | 1.7 | 4.4 | 1.5 | 2.0 | 3.5 | 5.6 | 3.1 | 1.8 |
| Bangladesh | 83.8 | 3.7 | 3.9 | 1.3 | 2.6 | 1.7 | 0.7 | 1.2 | 1.1 |
| Cambodia | 84.7 | 1.1 | 0.8 | 2.1 | 2.3 | 3.6 | 3.4 | 0.2 | 1.8 |
| China | 67.9 | 2.7 | 4.6 | 5.5 | 2.5 | 4.8 | 9.2 | 0.5 | 2.5 |
| Hong Kong | 33.5 | 8.2 | 16.5 | 1.5 | 3.7 | 7.3 | 17.7 | 2.9 | 8.6 |
| India | 63.3 | 9.8 | 6.6 | 1.7 | 7.2 | 4.2 | 0.9 | 4.5 | 1.7 |
| Indonesia | 66.4 | 4.9 | 7.5 | 5.8 | 8.9 | 2.6 | 1.9 | 0.3 | 1.8 |
| Iran, Islamic Rep. | 58.1 | 8.1 | 10.3 | 2.8 | 3.6 | 8.3 | 3.7 | 2.8 | 2.3 |
| Iraq | 62.1 | 11.0 | 9.2 | 1.2 | 1.9 | 8.6 | 2.3 | 2.3 | 1.4 |
| Israel | 32.7 | 12.5 | 16.6 | 1.8 | 6.5 | 10.1 | 8.4 | 7.7 | 3.7 |
| Japan | 40.4 | 10.6 | 9.5 | 2.7 | 4.5 | 10.9 | 6.3 | 3.8 | 11.3 |
| Jordan | 50.1 | 14.6 | 11.1 | 1.0 | 5.1 | 5.5 | 5.6 | 4.7 | 2.3 |
| Korea, Dem. People's Rep. | 63.7 | 4.0 | 3.3 | 5.4 | 7.6 | 8.6 | 3.3 | 0.2 | 3.8 |
| Korea, Rep. | 51.8 | 8.7 | 7.5 | 0.8 | 3.8 | 14.4 | 5.9 | 0.8 | 6.2 |
| Kuwait | 39.3 | 12.7 | 13.4 | 1.1 | 2.7 | 7.9 | 11.5 | 6.8 | 4.6 |
| Laos | 70.8 | 1.4 | 1.2 | 5.4 | 4.5 | 5.3 | 8.1 | 0.5 | 2.5 |
| Lebanon | 35.6 | 10.0 | 11.7 | 3.5 | 7.2 | 17.4 | 4.5 | 4.4 | 5.6 |
| Malaysia | 42.2 | 12.8 | 18.0 | 2.6 | 3.7 | 4.5 | 8.1 | 3.6 | 4.4 |
| Mongolia | 42.7 | 9.7 | 1.1 | 1.7 | 0.3 | 1.6 | 29.5 | 8.0 | 5.4 |
| Myanmar | 79.5 | 2.0 | 7.4 | 0.4 | 4.0 | 2.8 | 1.7 | 0.8 | 1.4 |
| Nepal | 77.6 | 3.0 | 4.0 | 3.0 | 2.9 | 3.2 | 1.4 | 3.4 | 1.4 |
| | | | | | | | | | *(continued)* |

*(continued)*

**TABLE 3**

| | | | SHARE OF MAJOR FOOD GROUPS IN TOTAL DIETARY ENERGY SUPPLY, 1990-92 | | | | | | | |

| | | | Share in total DES | | | | | | |
| | Vegetable products | | | | | | Animal products | | |
| | Cereals | Sugar | Vegetable oils | Roots and tubers | Pulses and nuts | Others | Meat and offal | Milk | Others |
|---|---|---|---|---|---|---|---|---|---|
| | | | | *(Percentage)* | | | | | |
| Pakistan | 55.8 | 12.8 | 11.3 | 0.4 | 2.4 | 3.1 | 2.9 | 7.4 | 3.7 |
| Philippines | 55.4 | 11.6 | 4.7 | 4.3 | 1.6 | 10.5 | 6.1 | 1.0 | 4.7 |
| Saudi Arabia | 41.9 | 10.8 | 14.0 | 0.8 | 2.3 | 12.5 | 8.3 | 6.2 | 3.2 |
| Sri Lanka | 58.1 | 10.3 | 2.9 | 2.4 | 15.1 | 6.3 | 0.6 | 2.4 | 1.8 |
| Syrian Arab Rep. | 53.4 | 10.1 | 12.0 | 1.3 | 5.2 | 6.4 | 3.6 | 5.3 | 2.7 |
| Thailand | 58.2 | 8.8 | 5.1 | 1.0 | 6.7 | 10.1 | 5.1 | 0.9 | 4.1 |
| Turkey | 49.4 | 7.8 | 12.8 | 3.3 | 6.3 | 9.0 | 2.5 | 6.6 | 2.3 |
| United Arab Emirates | 33.7 | 9.0 | 7.6 | 1.5 | 5.8 | 17.1 | 11.6 | 8.2 | 5.6 |
| Viet Nam | 72.7 | 3.2 | 1.6 | 7.1 | 2.1 | 5.2 | 5.8 | 0.1 | 2.1 |
| Yemen | 65.4 | 11.6 | 8.2 | 1.2 | 3.4 | 3.8 | 2.8 | 2.0 | 1.6 |
| **Europe** | **26.6** | **10.9** | **11.8** | **4.3** | **2.1** | **12.2** | **14.3** | **9.2** | **8.7** |
| Albania | 61.6 | 6.1 | 6.5 | 1.1 | 1.6 | 5.2 | 5.1 | 8.9 | 4.0 |
| Austria | 20.2 | 11.4 | 12.5 | 3.2 | 2.4 | 15.0 | 14.2 | 10.2 | 10.8 |
| Belgium/Luxembourg | 19.9 | 11.3 | 11.0 | 4.8 | 1.8 | 15.0 | 11.2 | 9.1 | 15.9 |
| Bulgaria | 41.3 | 6.7 | 10.7 | 1.9 | 2.3 | 12.2 | 10.8 | 8.0 | 6.1 |
| Czechoslovakia | 30.1 | 13.6 | 8.3 | 4.4 | 1.1 | 11.9 | 12.7 | 6.8 | 11.0 |
| Denmark | 20.6 | 11.5 | 5.8 | 3.3 | 1.2 | 13.3 | 24.2 | 7.5 | 12.6 |
| Finland | 23.9 | 12.4 | 6.2 | 4.8 | 1.1 | 11.9 | 16.9 | 14.3 | 8.5 |
| France | 22.9 | 10.1 | 10.8 | 3.5 | 1.8 | 11.2 | 18.4 | 11.5 | 10.0 |
| Germany | 20.6 | 12.7 | 9.8 | 4.1 | 1.8 | 15.8 | 14.6 | 9.5 | 11.1 |
| Greece | 28.7 | 8.4 | 17.8 | 3.8 | 3.8 | 13.4 | 11.9 | 9.1 | 3.2 |
| Hungary | 28.8 | 10.7 | 7.8 | 2.9 | 0.9 | 12.9 | 12.9 | 7.5 | 15.7 |
| Ireland | 26.0 | 11.5 | 10.9 | 6.1 | 1.4 | 10.5 | 13.5 | 13.0 | 7.2 |
| Italy | 32.0 | 8.2 | 17.6 | 2.2 | 2.7 | 12.1 | 11.4 | 7.4 | 6.4 |
| Netherlands | 16.7 | 16.9 | 13.4 | 5.3 | 2.7 | 14.0 | 11.9 | 11.5 | 7.6 |
| Norway | 27.3 | 12.9 | 11.1 | 4.5 | 1.3 | 9.6 | 11.1 | 11.8 | 10.4 |
| Poland | 33.7 | 11.8 | 5.5 | 7.7 | 0.8 | 7.1 | 12.9 | 10.2 | 10.2 |
| Portugal | 28.3 | 8.7 | 13.8 | 6.3 | 2.6 | 15.2 | 14.1 | 6.2 | 5.0 |
| Romania | 45.4 | 9.1 | 7.9 | 3.1 | 0.9 | 9.3 | 8.8 | 8.2 | 7.4 |
| Spain | 20.1 | 8.1 | 18.4 | 5.5 | 3.3 | 13.2 | 20.4 | 6.5 | 4.5 |
| Sweden | 22.0 | 14.4 | 10.7 | 4.4 | 1.8 | 10.6 | 10.2 | 15.3 | 10.5 |
| Switzerland | 21.5 | 12.3 | 9.3 | 2.5 | 2.7 | 13.8 | 18.1 | 11.7 | 8.0 |
| United Kingdom | 22.0 | 12.7 | 13.1 | 5.9 | 2.7 | 11.2 | 14.8 | 10.1 | 7.4 |
| Yugoslavia, SFR | 44.9 | 10.5 | 8.8 | 2.5 | 1.8 | 7.9 | 8.2 | 7.6 | 7.8 |
| **Oceania** | **22.1** | **12.7** | **9.6** | **6.0** | **3.0** | **12.8** | **17.2** | **10.3** | **6.2** |
| Australia | 21.6 | 14.2 | 10.7 | 3.1 | 2.6 | 11.1 | 19.3 | 12.1 | 5.4 |
| New Zealand | 23.6 | 14.4 | 6.5 | 2.8 | 2.4 | 10.5 | 17.1 | 10.3 | 12.5 |
| Papua New Guinea | 23.4 | 2.7 | 7.5 | 25.6 | 5.9 | 25.0 | 6.1 | 0.6 | 3.2 |
| **USSR** | **40.5** | **12.9** | **6.3** | **4.9** | **1.1** | **7.3** | **10.5** | **8.0** | **8.4** |

TABLE 4

| SHARE OF MAJOR FOOD GROUPS IN TOTAL DIETARY PROTEIN SUPPLY, 1990-92 | | | | | | | | |
|---|---|---|---|---|---|---|---|---|
| | Share in total protein supply | | | | | | | |
| | Vegetable products | | | | Animal products | | | |
| | Cereals | Pulses and nuts | Vegetables and fruits | Others | Meat and offal | Milk | Fish | Others |
| | *(Percentage)* | | | | | | | |
| **WORLD** | 47.2 | 8.3 | 4.8 | 4.2 | 17.2 | 9.6 | 5.9 | 2.8 |
| **Africa** | 53.5 | 13.2 | 4.6 | 7.4 | 10.8 | 5.7 | 3.8 | 1.0 |
| Algeria | 63.1 | 4.6 | 3.9 | 2.8 | 8.9 | 13.4 | 1.4 | 1.8 |
| Angola | 35.6 | 12.2 | 4.2 | 12.6 | 15.3 | 6.6 | 13.2 | 0.3 |
| Benin | 39.3 | 19.0 | 3.5 | 20.6 | 10.2 | 1.0 | 5.0 | 1.4 |
| Botswana | 42.4 | 9.5 | 2.3 | 3.4 | 23.2 | 16.4 | 1.9 | 0.8 |
| Burkina Faso | 71.1 | 13.1 | 1.5 | 2.5 | 7.9 | 2.4 | 0.9 | 0.5 |
| Burundi | 16.7 | 57.5 | 6.9 | 12.3 | 3.3 | 1.3 | 1.7 | 0.2 |
| Cameroon | 42.7 | 13.9 | 6.7 | 12.8 | 14.1 | 3.2 | 6.0 | 0.5 |
| Central African Rep. | 23.9 | 19.9 | 5.0 | 17.2 | 25.9 | 3.9 | 3.7 | 0.5 |
| Chad | 46.7 | 19.1 | 1.5 | 5.4 | 14.0 | 4.3 | 8.8 | 0.3 |
| Congo | 28.1 | 12.6 | 4.8 | 12.8 | 18.3 | 1.3 | 21.6 | 0.3 |
| Côte d'Ivoire | 41.5 | 10.1 | 6.6 | 19.5 | 10.3 | 2.6 | 8.9 | 0.5 |
| Egypt | 67.9 | 7.8 | 7.0 | 2.3 | 8.0 | 3.7 | 2.4 | 0.8 |
| Ethiopia, PDR | 59.1 | 21.1 | 0.9 | 3.6 | 10.9 | 3.6 | 0.0 | 0.8 |
| Gabon | 26.8 | 8.0 | 8.7 | 11.9 | 28.2 | 2.6 | 13.3 | 0.5 |
| Gambia | 62.2 | 12.1 | 2.3 | 2.3 | 10.9 | 2.5 | 7.4 | 0.4 |
| Ghana | 35.7 | 4.6 | 4.9 | 23.3 | 11.1 | 0.9 | 19.1 | 0.5 |
| Guinea | 50.4 | 12.5 | 17.7 | 6.3 | 5.4 | 2.0 | 4.6 | 1.0 |
| Kenya | 50.1 | 8.3 | 2.7 | 5.3 | 13.9 | 14.7 | 4.2 | 0.7 |
| Lesotho | 74.3 | 6.5 | 1.8 | 1.3 | 13.0 | 2.1 | 0.8 | 0.2 |
| Liberia | 48.6 | 11.2 | 6.4 | 11.0 | 10.3 | 0.6 | 10.7 | 1.2 |
| Libyan Arab Jam. | 49.3 | 6.4 | 8.1 | 3.0 | 14.7 | 14.7 | 1.3 | 2.5 |
| Madagascar | 51.9 | 4.3 | 3.7 | 10.4 | 18.9 | 6.4 | 3.7 | 0.8 |
| Malawi | 65.4 | 19.4 | 3.0 | 2.7 | 3.0 | 0.9 | 5.2 | 0.5 |
| Mali | 65.0 | 7.4 | 1.5 | 1.4 | 13.3 | 7.6 | 3.4 | 0.3 |
| Mauritania | 47.9 | 9.0 | 0.7 | 0.9 | 17.1 | 18.9 | 4.8 | 0.7 |
| Mauritius | 43.5 | 9.6 | 2.4 | 3.1 | 15.9 | 14.7 | 9.5 | 1.3 |
| Morocco | 67.6 | 7.9 | 4.1 | 3.1 | 8.9 | 3.8 | 2.6 | 2.1 |
| Mozambique | 52.1 | 14.2 | 2.2 | 18.7 | 7.7 | 1.9 | 2.7 | 0.5 |
| Namibia | 47.1 | 8.8 | 1.8 | 9.7 | 22.6 | 5.4 | 4.3 | 0.4 |
| Niger | 59.7 | 21.6 | 1.7 | 1.7 | 9.8 | 4.8 | 0.4 | 0.4 |
| Nigeria | 47.5 | 21.5 | 5.7 | 13.2 | 7.0 | 0.9 | 2.7 | 1.5 |
| Rwanda | 21.5 | 45.1 | 8.0 | 17.9 | 4.3 | 2.9 | 0.1 | 0.2 |
| Senegal | 61.1 | 8.4 | 1.2 | 1.3 | 11.1 | 6.4 | 9.8 | 0.9 |
| Sierra Leone | 53.4 | 18.4 | 5.4 | 3.9 | 5.3 | 1.5 | 11.1 | 0.9 |
| Somalia | 47.3 | 3.4 | 1.4 | 0.3 | 14.9 | 31.6 | 0.9 | 0.2 |
| South Africa | 56.4 | 2.6 | 2.6 | 2.8 | 22.6 | 7.2 | 3.9 | 2.0 |
| Sudan | 57.4 | 4.8 | 2.2 | 1.3 | 12.3 | 21.1 | 0.4 | 0.6 |
| Swaziland | 58.2 | 7.0 | 3.2 | 1.6 | 20.9 | 7.6 | 0.1 | 1.4 |
| Togo | 56.4 | 9.4 | 3.5 | 14.6 | 7.7 | 1.1 | 6.7 | 0.7 |
| Tunisia | 62.0 | 7.9 | 6.3 | 2.8 | 8.2 | 7.9 | 3.3 | 1.8 |
| Uganda | 17.1 | 36.5 | 10.2 | 15.2 | 8.8 | 3.8 | 8.0 | 0.3 |
| United Rep. of Tanzania | 44.7 | 14.6 | 5.0 | 13.1 | 9.2 | 3.9 | 8.6 | 0.9 |
| Zaire | 24.2 | 23.7 | 9.9 | 22.9 | 12.3 | 0.2 | 6.6 | 0.2 |
| Zambia | 72.3 | 3.7 | 2.3 | 4.4 | 10.0 | 1.5 | 4.2 | 1.6 |
| Zimbabwe | 62.6 | 15.7 | 1.4 | 1.4 | 10.4 | 6.9 | 0.9 | 0.8 |
| **North and Central America** | 27.9 | 6.6 | 4.3 | 4.2 | 31.9 | 17.3 | 4.3 | 3.6 |
| Canada | 21.5 | 7.8 | 5.3 | 5.2 | 34.4 | 16.7 | 5.6 | 3.4 |
| Costa Rica | 32.5 | 12.2 | 4.0 | 3.5 | 23.9 | 18.6 | 3.2 | 2.2 |

*(continued)*

*(continued)*

**TABLE 4**

| | | | | | | | | |
|---|---|---|---|---|---|---|---|---|
| **SHARE OF MAJOR FOOD GROUPS IN TOTAL DIETARY PROTEIN SUPPLY, 1990-92** | | | | | | | | |
| | Share in total protein supply | | | | | | | |
| | Vegetable products | | | | Animal products | | | |
| | Cereals | Pulses and nuts | Vegetables and fruits | Others | Meat and offal | Milk | Fish | Others |
| | *(Percentage)* | | | | | | | |
| Cuba | 34.4 | 11.1 | 3.5 | 2.7 | 21.6 | 15.9 | 7.1 | 3.6 |
| Dominican Rep. | 34.1 | 12.3 | 7.3 | 4.1 | 21.6 | 13.9 | 4.3 | 2.4 |
| El Salvador | 59.1 | 13.4 | 2.9 | 1.5 | 8.3 | 10.3 | 0.8 | 3.7 |
| Guatemala | 63.5 | 14.4 | 2.4 | 1.2 | 8.6 | 6.4 | 0.4 | 3.1 |
| Haiti | 44.6 | 26.0 | 6.9 | 6.4 | 9.2 | 3.4 | 3.1 | 0.4 |
| Honduras | 52.7 | 15.9 | 3.7 | 1.4 | 10.0 | 12.9 | 0.9 | 2.6 |
| Jamaica | 37.5 | 4.8 | 4.3 | 7.9 | 24.1 | 8.1 | 8.4 | 4.9 |
| Mexico | 46.9 | 10.9 | 3.3 | 1.9 | 19.3 | 10.4 | 3.5 | 3.8 |
| Nicaragua | 48.1 | 21.9 | 2.1 | 2.2 | 11.2 | 10.6 | 0.5 | 3.3 |
| Panama | 33.7 | 7.6 | 4.3 | 2.9 | 29.6 | 13.5 | 6.5 | 2.0 |
| Trinidad and Tobago | 39.9 | 12.0 | 3.1 | 4.1 | 18.0 | 14.4 | 5.5 | 3.0 |
| United States | 21.7 | 4.5 | 4.5 | 4.8 | 36.7 | 19.7 | 4.4 | 3.6 |
| **South America** | **33.9** | **10.3** | **4.1** | **5.2** | **27.3** | **13.0** | **3.3** | **3.0** |
| Argentina | 24.4 | 1.4 | 2.9 | 5.8 | 46.1 | 15.2 | 1.7 | 2.5 |
| Bolivia | 39.0 | 7.7 | 6.1 | 10.9 | 27.6 | 4.2 | 0.7 | 3.9 |
| Brazil | 34.0 | 15.9 | 4.0 | 4.2 | 23.1 | 12.7 | 2.7 | 3.4 |
| Chile | 42.0 | 3.3 | 5.4 | 5.0 | 21.3 | 13.0 | 7.4 | 2.5 |
| Colombia | 33.8 | 7.7 | 4.8 | 8.3 | 24.3 | 16.8 | 1.2 | 3.1 |
| Ecuador | 44.0 | 4.8 | 4.8 | 4.8 | 20.4 | 12.3 | 6.4 | 2.6 |
| Guyana | 45.4 | 8.4 | 2.9 | 1.7 | 14.2 | 6.1 | 17.6 | 3.8 |
| Paraguay | 23.6 | 12.2 | 4.6 | 9.3 | 38.1 | 7.6 | 1.4 | 3.2 |
| Peru | 42.1 | 6.1 | 4.8 | 6.9 | 20.2 | 7.6 | 10.0 | 2.3 |
| Suriname | 46.3 | 5.6 | 4.4 | 2.5 | 20.7 | 14.2 | 3.5 | 2.8 |
| Uruguay | 28.0 | 2.3 | 2.5 | 5.7 | 40.5 | 17.4 | 1.8 | 1.8 |
| Venezuela | 40.1 | 7.2 | 3.9 | 3.7 | 25.4 | 11.8 | 5.7 | 2.1 |
| **Asia** | **57.9** | **9.8** | **5.2** | **2.9** | **10.2** | **5.2** | **6.3** | **2.5** |
| Afghanistan | 70.7 | 3.4 | 2.9 | 1.3 | 13.9 | 7.3 | 0.1 | 0.5 |
| Bangladesh | 77.8 | 7.2 | 1.4 | 2.4 | 3.0 | 2.8 | 5.0 | 0.4 |
| Cambodia | 71.5 | 5.7 | 4.6 | 1.6 | 8.0 | 0.4 | 7.5 | 0.8 |
| China | 61.3 | 6.2 | 5.8 | 3.2 | 14.7 | 1.1 | 4.4 | 3.4 |
| Hong Kong | 23.2 | 7.2 | 3.9 | 1.9 | 37.7 | 4.5 | 16.9 | 4.8 |
| India | 61.2 | 15.0 | 4.8 | 2.8 | 3.2 | 10.2 | 2.1 | 0.7 |
| Indonesia | 58.2 | 21.6 | 2.5 | 2.2 | 4.7 | 0.7 | 8.9 | 1.3 |
| Iran, Islamic Rep. | 62.3 | 7.3 | 6.1 | 2.4 | 11.1 | 7.2 | 1.7 | 2.0 |
| Iraq | 70.5 | 4.3 | 8.4 | 1.4 | 7.1 | 6.6 | 0.5 | 1.3 |
| Israel | 31.6 | 8.1 | 6.3 | 2.7 | 24.6 | 16.8 | 4.7 | 5.2 |
| Japan | 23.2 | 9.6 | 4.9 | 3.4 | 15.0 | 6.9 | 30.4 | 6.6 |
| Jordan | 54.1 | 8.0 | 5.3 | 1.6 | 17.3 | 9.4 | 1.0 | 3.4 |
| Korea, Dem. People's Rep. | 45.9 | 19.9 | 8.4 | 3.9 | 5.2 | 0.4 | 14.0 | 2.3 |
| Korea, Rep. | 39.5 | 11.0 | 10.3 | 2.1 | 11.4 | 2.2 | 20.1 | 3.4 |
| Kuwait | 35.5 | 4.1 | 6.5 | 3.2 | 29.4 | 15.5 | 3.3 | 2.5 |
| Laos | 60.2 | 10.0 | 3.3 | 2.8 | 16.2 | 0.8 | 3.2 | 3.5 |
| Lebanon | 35.6 | 13.4 | 14.7 | 4.4 | 14.0 | 12.1 | 0.2 | 5.6 |
| Malaysia | 40.4 | 5.1 | 3.2 | 3.3 | 22.7 | 6.2 | 11.3 | 7.7 |
| Mongolia | 30.2 | 0.6 | 0.6 | 2.0 | 53.5 | 12.3 | 0.5 | 0.4 |
| Myanmar | 75.3 | 7.8 | 3.3 | 0.9 | 4.0 | 2.4 | 5.9 | 0.4 |
| Nepal | 71.7 | 7.2 | 3.9 | 3.6 | 5.8 | 6.8 | 0.4 | 0.5 |
| Pakistan | 58.2 | 5.8 | 2.9 | 2.4 | 10.0 | 18.8 | 1.1 | 0.9 |
| Philippines | 46.5 | 2.9 | 6.9 | 3.2 | 12.5 | 3.3 | 21.7 | 2.9 |

*(continued)*

(continued)

**TABLE 4**

## SHARE OF MAJOR FOOD GROUPS IN TOTAL DIETARY PROTEIN SUPPLY, 1990-92

| | Share in total protein supply | | | | | | | |
|---|---|---|---|---|---|---|---|---|
| | Vegetable products | | | | Animal products | | | |
| | Cereals | Pulses and nuts | Vegetables and fruits | Others | Meat and offal | Milk | Fish | Others |
| | *(Percentage)* | | | | | | | |
| Saudi Arabia | 41.5 | 4.1 | 8.3 | 2.1 | 25.3 | 13.3 | 2.4 | 3.1 |
| Sri Lanka | 58.1 | 13.6 | 4.4 | 5.2 | 3.0 | 6.1 | 8.0 | 1.6 |
| Syrian Arab Rep. | 60.7 | 9.3 | 5.6 | 2.0 | 9.2 | 11.1 | 0.2 | 1.9 |
| Thailand | 46.9 | 11.6 | 4.5 | 1.0 | 14.2 | 2.6 | 14.3 | 4.9 |
| Turkey | 53.5 | 9.8 | 7.6 | 3.9 | 7.6 | 13.6 | 2.0 | 2.0 |
| United Arab Emirates | 26.4 | 7.3 | 11.7 | 3.5 | 26.8 | 14.2 | 6.1 | 3.9 |
| Viet Nam | 64.9 | 4.8 | 5.3 | 3.6 | 11.3 | 0.3 | 8.3 | 1.6 |
| Yemen | 70.5 | 7.1 | 2.7 | 1.3 | 7.9 | 6.3 | 3.4 | 0.8 |
| **Europe** | **27.6** | **3.1** | **5.2** | **6.0** | **29.6** | **18.9** | **5.6** | **4.0** |
| Albania | 60.6 | 2.8 | 5.2 | 1.1 | 11.2 | 16.7 | 0.8 | 1.6 |
| Austria | 21.2 | 3.4 | 4.5 | 7.1 | 34.4 | 22.5 | 2.7 | 4.3 |
| Belgium/Luxembourg | 22.0 | 2.8 | 5.1 | 7.9 | 30.8 | 22.2 | 5.3 | 4.0 |
| Bulgaria | 42.8 | 3.6 | 4.5 | 2.8 | 26.2 | 15.2 | 0.9 | 3.9 |
| Czechoslovakia | 33.0 | 1.9 | 3.5 | 6.5 | 31.7 | 15.8 | 2.0 | 5.5 |
| Denmark | 22.2 | 1.8 | 4.2 | 7.5 | 30.5 | 17.8 | 11.2 | 4.9 |
| Finland | 23.6 | 1.8 | 3.2 | 7.6 | 23.8 | 27.4 | 9.1 | 3.6 |
| France | 21.7 | 2.4 | 4.7 | 4.4 | 34.0 | 22.9 | 5.7 | 4.2 |
| Germany | 21.1 | 2.3 | 4.9 | 7.5 | 32.8 | 21.0 | 5.8 | 4.6 |
| Greece | 30.3 | 5.0 | 9.2 | 4.0 | 24.0 | 19.3 | 5.3 | 2.9 |
| Hungary | 34.3 | 1.8 | 4.7 | 6.5 | 29.4 | 14.9 | 1.2 | 7.1 |
| Ireland | 24.1 | 2.4 | 3.1 | 6.8 | 36.2 | 20.9 | 4.0 | 2.4 |
| Italy | 32.3 | 4.0 | 7.2 | 3.0 | 29.8 | 14.4 | 5.7 | 3.6 |
| Netherlands | 18.0 | 3.9 | 4.7 | 8.8 | 30.6 | 26.3 | 3.5 | 4.2 |
| Norway | 27.1 | 1.6 | 3.4 | 7.1 | 18.4 | 22.9 | 15.8 | 3.7 |
| Poland | 33.7 | 1.5 | 4.3 | 7.3 | 27.6 | 18.0 | 4.5 | 3.1 |
| Portugal | 29.5 | 4.3 | 6.7 | 7.2 | 24.4 | 13.7 | 11.8 | 2.4 |
| Romania | 45.4 | 1.3 | 4.1 | 3.7 | 22.5 | 15.8 | 3.3 | 3.9 |
| Spain | 22.2 | 5.1 | 7.5 | 6.7 | 31.5 | 12.6 | 9.7 | 4.6 |
| Sweden | 20.4 | 2.2 | 3.7 | 6.8 | 23.1 | 30.3 | 9.2 | 4.3 |
| Switzerland | 24.0 | 3.2 | 5.0 | 4.7 | 30.2 | 25.1 | 3.9 | 3.8 |
| United Kingdom | 25.0 | 5.0 | 4.4 | 8.4 | 28.2 | 20.0 | 5.3 | 3.6 |
| Yugoslavia, SFR | 49.3 | 3.3 | 3.6 | 3.6 | 20.9 | 14.9 | 1.7 | 2.7 |
| **Oceania** | **20.8** | **3.7** | **5.1** | **5.4** | **36.5** | **19.2** | **6.8** | **2.6** |
| Australia | 20.2 | 3.7 | 3.7 | 4.5 | 39.7 | 21.3 | 4.3 | 2.6 |
| New Zealand | 21.2 | 3.5 | 3.7 | 3.9 | 30.6 | 18.9 | 14.8 | 3.4 |
| Papua New Guinea | 25.0 | 4.0 | 20.3 | 16.7 | 19.7 | 1.3 | 12.4 | 0.5 |
| **USSR** | **39.1** | **1.9** | **3.1** | **4.5** | **22.7** | **14.2** | **10.2** | **4.3** |

TABLE 5

| SHARE OF MAJOR FOOD GROUPS IN TOTAL DIETARY FAT SUPPLY, 1990-92 | | | | | | | |
|---|---|---|---|---|---|---|---|
| | | | | Share in total fat supply | | | |
| | Vegetable products | | | | Animal products | | |
| | Vegetable oils | Cereals | Pulses and nuts | Others | Meat and offal | Milk | Animal fats | Others |
| | | | | (Percentage) | | | |
| **WORLD** | 36.6 | 8.3 | 6.1 | 2.3 | 23.9 | 9.7 | 9.0 | 4.1 |
| **Africa** | 46.5 | 16.6 | 9.5 | 3.4 | 11.0 | 6.5 | 4.4 | 2.1 |
| Algeria | 59.7 | 8.3 | 0.8 | 1.2 | 9.2 | 10.7 | 8.1 | 2.0 |
| Angola | 57.6 | 9.1 | 4.4 | 2.3 | 15.5 | 3.8 | 3.7 | 3.4 |
| Benin | 42.3 | 15.0 | 23.3 | 6.7 | 7.6 | 1.1 | 1.3 | 2.6 |
| Botswana | 27.0 | 12.7 | 1.7 | 3.3 | 16.4 | 15.2 | 22.6 | 1.0 |
| Burkina Faso | 22.8 | 35.0 | 24.9 | 1.4 | 9.2 | 3.4 | 2.4 | 0.8 |
| Burundi | 17.1 | 23.9 | 21.8 | 11.8 | 14.2 | 4.7 | 4.0 | 2.5 |
| Cameroon | 45.1 | 14.1 | 16.0 | 5.7 | 11.7 | 3.8 | 1.6 | 2.1 |
| Central African Rep. | 48.3 | 4.7 | 22.0 | 2.5 | 15.5 | 2.7 | 3.5 | 0.8 |
| Chad | 24.7 | 16.9 | 36.0 | 1.4 | 11.3 | 6.2 | 2.5 | 1.0 |
| Congo | 52.3 | 4.4 | 15.2 | 8.6 | 12.5 | 1.1 | 1.3 | 4.5 |
| Côte d'Ivoire | 52.9 | 10.2 | 17.0 | 6.3 | 8.7 | 0.9 | 1.5 | 2.7 |
| Egypt | 43.5 | 23.8 | 4.1 | 2.8 | 8.8 | 4.5 | 10.9 | 1.7 |
| Ethiopia, PDR | 21.7 | 31.0 | 16.2 | 3.1 | 14.7 | 6.7 | 5.4 | 1.3 |
| Gabon | 35.9 | 7.5 | 18.8 | 4.3 | 22.7 | 3.4 | 2.4 | 4.9 |
| Gambia | 56.1 | 13.0 | 16.7 | 0.6 | 7.9 | 2.3 | 1.8 | 1.6 |
| Ghana | 48.4 | 14.2 | 16.5 | 5.7 | 7.3 | 0.5 | 1.3 | 6.2 |
| Guinea | 67.3 | 10.4 | 7.8 | 5.6 | 4.1 | 2.4 | 0.6 | 1.9 |
| Kenya | 39.6 | 20.0 | 3.1 | 1.3 | 12.5 | 18.3 | 3.5 | 1.6 |
| Lesotho | 22.5 | 47.5 | 0.7 | 1.9 | 18.7 | 4.5 | 3.5 | 0.8 |
| Liberia | 73.5 | 6.0 | 7.4 | 2.2 | 6.7 | 0.4 | 0.7 | 3.1 |
| Libyan Arab Jam. | 60.7 | 4.4 | 9.5 | 1.6 | 9.6 | 8.5 | 3.9 | 1.9 |
| Madagascar | 24.0 | 15.3 | 5.3 | 5.5 | 31.6 | 10.9 | 5.1 | 2.4 |
| Malawi | 15.0 | 57.4 | 10.5 | 2.6 | 8.4 | 1.5 | 1.1 | 3.5 |
| Mali | 33.6 | 31.1 | 6.4 | 0.8 | 12.3 | 12.1 | 2.2 | 1.5 |
| Mauritania | 34.9 | 9.1 | 3.6 | 0.4 | 16.6 | 28.0 | 5.6 | 1.7 |
| Mauritius | 58.5 | 3.9 | 2.1 | 2.3 | 13.6 | 12.1 | 3.8 | 3.7 |
| Morocco | 48.8 | 15.0 | 7.3 | 3.0 | 10.3 | 2.9 | 9.1 | 3.6 |
| Mozambique | 64.9 | 14.4 | 8.2 | 2.3 | 6.8 | 1.3 | 1.1 | 1.0 |
| Namibia | 21.0 | 23.5 | 1.5 | 3.5 | 28.3 | 11.3 | 9.3 | 1.6 |
| Niger | 23.7 | 42.2 | 5.9 | 2.1 | 12.2 | 7.6 | 5.6 | 0.7 |
| Nigeria | 64.0 | 12.7 | 9.7 | 5.1 | 5.1 | 0.4 | 1.5 | 1.6 |
| Rwanda | 31.6 | 19.7 | 16.7 | 11.8 | 8.7 | 8.9 | 2.3 | 0.4 |
| Senegal | 52.4 | 14.0 | 14.4 | 1.0 | 9.4 | 3.1 | 2.4 | 3.4 |
| Sierra Leone | 79.4 | 4.5 | 8.8 | 1.9 | 2.4 | 0.9 | 0.4 | 1.9 |
| Somalia | 18.8 | 17.9 | 4.2 | 0.8 | 12.9 | 39.2 | 6.0 | 0.3 |
| South Africa | 42.8 | 15.2 | 1.0 | 1.3 | 25.8 | 8.0 | 2.9 | 2.8 |
| Sudan | 32.0 | 19.9 | 5.4 | 0.8 | 11.7 | 26.0 | 3.6 | 0.6 |
| Swaziland | 39.9 | 12.7 | 7.9 | 2.3 | 21.3 | 10.6 | 3.9 | 1.4 |
| Togo | 47.1 | 20.6 | 14.1 | 3.5 | 9.0 | 1.1 | 1.8 | 2.8 |
| Tunisia | 64.9 | 7.3 | 5.9 | 2.7 | 6.6 | 6.9 | 3.6 | 2.2 |
| Uganda | 14.4 | 7.7 | 34.4 | 7.8 | 19.5 | 7.9 | 4.5 | 3.8 |
| United Rep. of Tanzania | 37.0 | 16.3 | 11.5 | 6.1 | 12.7 | 6.3 | 5.7 | 4.4 |
| Zaire | 46.7 | 7.1 | 29.1 | 7.8 | 6.7 | 0.1 | 1.0 | 1.6 |
| Zambia | 18.3 | 51.8 | 5.6 | 2.3 | 12.6 | 2.9 | 2.3 | 4.2 |
| Zimbabwe | 34.8 | 21.6 | 15.7 | 0.4 | 8.5 | 7.6 | 10.6 | 0.8 |
| **North and Central America** | 40.2 | 4.5 | 4.4 | 1.8 | 25.1 | 12.8 | 8.1 | 3.1 |
| Canada | 36.4 | 2.1 | 5.0 | 1.7 | 26.5 | 13.1 | 11.8 | 3.5 |
| Costa Rica | 48.2 | 5.2 | 3.0 | 3.2 | 17.6 | 14.0 | 6.9 | 2.0 |

(continued)

104

(continued)

## TABLE 5

| | SHARE OF MAJOR FOOD GROUPS IN TOTAL DIETARY FAT SUPPLY, 1990-92 | | | | | | | |
|---|---|---|---|---|---|---|---|---|
| | **Share in total fat supply** | | | | | | | |
| | **Vegetable products** | | | | **Animal products** | | | |
| | Vegetable oils | Cereals | Pulses and nuts | Others | Meat and offal | Milk | Animal fats | Others |
| | *(Percentage)* | | | | | | | |
| Cuba | 40.6 | 2.8 | 2.5 | 1.5 | 19.4 | 8.5 | 21.0 | 3.7 |
| Dominican Rep. | 58.7 | 3.0 | 2.3 | 6.1 | 15.6 | 6.5 | 5.5 | 2.4 |
| El Salvador | 31.8 | 22.8 | 10.1 | 4.5 | 5.7 | 11.2 | 10.3 | 3.7 |
| Guatemala | 32.5 | 35.1 | 5.2 | 2.2 | 7.9 | 8.7 | 4.7 | 3.8 |
| Haiti | 22.9 | 14.5 | 29.6 | 10.4 | 14.1 | 3.5 | 3.9 | 1.1 |
| Honduras | 44.5 | 18.7 | 4.1 | 2.1 | 6.3 | 9.8 | 12.3 | 2.2 |
| Jamaica | 42.8 | 5.8 | 9.2 | 2.8 | 19.3 | 4.9 | 8.7 | 6.5 |
| Mexico | 39.4 | 14.1 | 3.3 | 1.8 | 21.1 | 7.9 | 8.8 | 3.6 |
| Nicaragua | 44.3 | 15.7 | 8.3 | 1.1 | 11.1 | 7.9 | 8.5 | 3.0 |
| Panama | 41.3 | 3.3 | 3.7 | 2.8 | 21.5 | 11.1 | 13.2 | 3.1 |
| Trinidad and Tobago | 46.2 | 3.6 | 5.9 | 2.1 | 15.1 | 10.0 | 14.2 | 2.9 |
| United States | 40.5 | 2.2 | 4.4 | 1.7 | 26.8 | 14.1 | 7.3 | 3.0 |
| **South America** | **45.9** | **4.0** | **3.1** | **1.9** | **24.4** | **10.9** | **7.1** | **2.8** |
| Argentina | 29.9 | 2.4 | 1.0 | 1.5 | 38.4 | 15.3 | 9.2 | 2.3 |
| Bolivia | 30.5 | 5.0 | 8.0 | 4.0 | 29.2 | 2.9 | 17.4 | 2.9 |
| Brazil | 50.5 | 3.3 | 3.9 | 1.6 | 21.6 | 9.9 | 6.6 | 2.7 |
| Chile | 39.2 | 6.0 | 1.2 | 2.8 | 28.6 | 11.6 | 6.0 | 4.6 |
| Colombia | 40.1 | 7.1 | 2.9 | 2.9 | 24.3 | 13.3 | 6.4 | 2.9 |
| Ecuador | 62.9 | 5.6 | 1.3 | 1.5 | 11.6 | 7.5 | 7.2 | 2.3 |
| Guyana | 24.8 | 7.2 | 16.4 | 2.1 | 25.5 | 9.8 | 2.0 | 12.2 |
| Paraguay | 41.3 | 4.5 | 2.8 | 2.4 | 32.3 | 5.6 | 9.0 | 2.2 |
| Peru | 37.3 | 9.1 | 3.6 | 4.8 | 22.4 | 10.1 | 6.1 | 6.6 |
| Suriname | 49.6 | 5.3 | 5.2 | 1.8 | 23.7 | 7.0 | 4.2 | 3.2 |
| Uruguay | 17.1 | 2.5 | 1.6 | 1.3 | 50.7 | 12.5 | 12.6 | 1.5 |
| Venezuela | 59.0 | 4.6 | 2.0 | 1.8 | 13.7 | 11.0 | 5.0 | 2.9 |
| **Asia** | **36.7** | **11.9** | **8.7** | **2.5** | **23.4** | **6.2** | **5.8** | **4.7** |
| Afghanistan | 27.7 | 20.5 | 6.2 | 1.6 | 24.1 | 9.3 | 10.0 | 0.7 |
| Bangladesh | 51.0 | 23.8 | 2.5 | 3.2 | 4.9 | 7.5 | 3.3 | 3.7 |
| Cambodia | 9.9 | 31.6 | 11.7 | 5.7 | 29.5 | 1.0 | 5.0 | 5.6 |
| China | 26.8 | 10.7 | 5.3 | 2.2 | 44.1 | 1.4 | 4.4 | 5.1 |
| Hong Kong | 42.2 | 1.9 | 4.3 | 2.1 | 32.5 | 2.4 | 10.1 | 4.5 |
| India | 42.6 | 16.5 | 11.5 | 2.8 | 3.2 | 14.1 | 7.9 | 1.4 |
| Indonesia | 44.6 | 12.5 | 26.7 | 2.3 | 8.2 | 0.7 | 1.9 | 3.2 |
| Iran, Islamic Rep. | 50.9 | 12.5 | 5.1 | 2.5 | 12.0 | 7.7 | 6.8 | 2.6 |
| Iraq | 54.4 | 15.9 | 4.3 | 2.6 | 9.3 | 6.4 | 5.3 | 1.7 |
| Israel | 49.3 | 3.3 | 11.1 | 3.2 | 14.6 | 11.7 | 1.9 | 4.9 |
| Japan | 38.9 | 4.4 | 7.1 | 2.7 | 16.6 | 6.9 | 4.7 | 18.7 |
| Jordan | 45.5 | 8.9 | 11.7 | 1.7 | 14.7 | 10.1 | 4.0 | 3.3 |
| Korea, Dem. People's Rep. | 26.7 | 22.5 | 10.6 | 4.6 | 21.3 | 0.9 | 2.9 | 10.5 |
| Korea, Rep. | 40.4 | 6.8 | 7.4 | 2.8 | 24.2 | 1.3 | 7.1 | 10.1 |
| Kuwait | 42.6 | 3.6 | 4.1 | 5.0 | 24.7 | 7.8 | 9.8 | 2.3 |
| Laos | 9.1 | 22.4 | 6.2 | 4.3 | 45.1 | 0.6 | 5.4 | 6.9 |
| Lebanon | 44.0 | 3.9 | 11.3 | 4.6 | 10.6 | 7.4 | 13.7 | 4.6 |
| Malaysia | 57.7 | 3.1 | 6.9 | 1.7 | 19.0 | 3.1 | 3.4 | 5.1 |
| Mongolia | 3.4 | 4.8 | 0.1 | 0.2 | 64.3 | 11.5 | 15.4 | 0.4 |
| Myanmar | 50.5 | 21.8 | 10.1 | 2.1 | 8.4 | 2.4 | 2.4 | 2.3 |
| Nepal | 33.2 | 29.1 | 2.4 | 4.1 | 5.7 | 14.7 | 9.8 | 1.0 |
| Pakistan | 48.8 | 10.8 | 1.7 | 1.3 | 7.8 | 14.4 | 14.3 | 0.9 |
| Philippines | 32.1 | 8.3 | 5.9 | 3.9 | 32.9 | 1.8 | 5.1 | 9.9 |

*105*

(continued)

*(continued)*

**TABLE 5**

| SHARE OF MAJOR FOOD GROUPS IN TOTAL DIETARY FAT SUPPLY, 1990-92 | | | | | | | |
|---|---|---|---|---|---|---|---|
| | Share in total fat supply | | | | | | |
| | Vegetable products | | | | Animal products | | |
| | Vegetable oils | Cereals | Pulses and nuts | Others | Meat and offal | Milk | Animal fats | Others |
| | *(Percentage)* | | | | | | | |
| Saudi Arabia | 48.8 | 7.8 | 3.2 | 4.2 | 17.8 | 9.6 | 5.5 | 3.1 |
| Sri Lanka | 16.5 | 7.8 | 57.5 | 4.3 | 1.9 | 6.7 | 1.8 | 3.4 |
| Syrian Arab Rep. | 46.6 | 9.7 | 11.0 | 1.6 | 9.7 | 12.1 | 7.6 | 1.7 |
| Thailand | 31.3 | 7.2 | 21.8 | 2.5 | 22.9 | 1.1 | 3.9 | 9.4 |
| Turkey | 54.1 | 7.2 | 8.3 | 2.8 | 6.6 | 13.4 | 5.2 | 2.4 |
| United Arab Emirates | 25.9 | 3.7 | 10.0 | 5.6 | 26.2 | 14.6 | 9.4 | 4.6 |
| Viet Nam | 14.5 | 20.0 | 6.7 | 5.5 | 41.1 | 0.5 | 7.2 | 4.4 |
| Yemen | 50.0 | 23.1 | 4.0 | 1.5 | 11.2 | 3.3 | 4.7 | 2.3 |
| **Europe** | **31.7** | **2.5** | **2.7** | **2.2** | **27.6** | **13.6** | **16.4** | **3.3** |
| Albania | 31.5 | 10.2 | 1.8 | 1.4 | 16.8 | 21.0 | 15.4 | 1.9 |
| Austria | 30.4 | 2.0 | 4.1 | 2.7 | 23.9 | 13.0 | 21.1 | 2.9 |
| Belgium/Luxembourg | 26.5 | 1.6 | 2.3 | 5.5 | 17.6 | 11.4 | 32.1 | 3.0 |
| Bulgaria | 34.9 | 4.0 | 3.1 | 1.7 | 23.6 | 15.2 | 14.5 | 3.0 |
| Czechoslovakia | 25.7 | 3.1 | 1.5 | 1.3 | 26.9 | 10.8 | 26.6 | 4.1 |
| Denmark | 13.2 | 1.9 | 1.7 | 2.9 | 46.3 | 9.9 | 20.2 | 4.0 |
| Finland | 16.9 | 2.9 | 1.5 | 2.1 | 37.0 | 20.9 | 14.5 | 4.2 |
| France | 25.6 | 2.3 | 2.3 | 1.9 | 32.1 | 15.5 | 17.1 | 3.2 |
| Germany | 26.1 | 2.1 | 3.2 | 2.4 | 27.4 | 13.0 | 22.1 | 3.8 |
| Greece | 47.3 | 2.7 | 5.0 | 2.1 | 22.8 | 14.6 | 3.1 | 2.4 |
| Hungary | 20.3 | 2.6 | 0.9 | 2.6 | 24.4 | 11.4 | 33.7 | 4.0 |
| Ireland | 31.2 | 2.5 | 1.3 | 2.7 | 24.0 | 20.2 | 15.6 | 2.5 |
| Italy | 47.6 | 2.6 | 2.8 | 1.6 | 19.9 | 11.7 | 10.6 | 3.2 |
| Netherlands | 35.7 | 1.6 | 4.0 | 4.3 | 21.3 | 15.7 | 14.6 | 2.8 |
| Norway | 29.7 | 2.8 | 2.2 | 3.5 | 22.8 | 18.0 | 13.3 | 7.7 |
| Poland | 17.4 | 3.3 | 0.3 | 1.5 | 29.2 | 19.0 | 26.2 | 3.0 |
| Portugal | 41.0 | 3.1 | 2.3 | 2.3 | 32.5 | 9.2 | 6.8 | 2.7 |
| Romania | 29.8 | 5.8 | 1.5 | 1.9 | 21.7 | 15.6 | 19.4 | 4.3 |
| Spain | 42.1 | 1.5 | 3.5 | 1.7 | 37.1 | 8.0 | 2.9 | 3.1 |
| Sweden | 28.9 | 3.0 | 3.1 | 2.7 | 18.7 | 20.4 | 17.7 | 5.5 |
| Switzerland | 22.2 | 1.9 | 4.7 | 4.8 | 34.0 | 15.5 | 14.2 | 2.7 |
| United Kingdom | 33.7 | 2.2 | 2.9 | 2.2 | 28.9 | 14.1 | 13.4 | 2.7 |
| Yugoslavia, SFR | 31.2 | 5.5 | 1.6 | 1.8 | 19.7 | 15.0 | 22.7 | 2.6 |
| **Oceania** | **27.5** | **2.1** | **4.6** | **2.1** | **34.9** | **14.1** | **11.9** | **2.8** |
| Australia | 28.9 | 2.1 | 3.2 | 1.4 | 36.8 | 15.7 | 9.5 | 2.5 |
| New Zealand | 17.1 | 2.0 | 3.2 | 2.3 | 33.0 | 13.2 | 25.9 | 3.3 |
| Papua New Guinea | 35.9 | 2.7 | 20.7 | 8.8 | 21.0 | 1.0 | 5.4 | 4.4 |
| **USSR** | **24.0** | **5.5** | **1.7** | **1.4** | **27.5** | **15.7** | **16.8** | **7.4** |

## TABLE 6

### SHARE OF MAIN CEREALS AND ROOTS IN TOTAL DIETARY ENERGY SUPPLY, 1969-71 AND 1990-92

| | Share in total DES | | | | | | | | | |
|---|---|---|---|---|---|---|---|---|---|---|
| | Rice | | Wheat | | Maize | | Sorghum and millet | | Cassava | |
| | 1969-71 | 1990-92 | 1969-71 | 1990-92 | 1969-71 | 1990-92 | 1969-71 | 1990-92 | 1969-71 | 1990-92 |
| | *(Percentage)* | | | | | | | | | |
| **WORLD** | 20.3 | 22.0 | 17.5 | 19.5 | 5.4 | 6.1 | 4.4 | 2.6 | 1.7 | 1.6 |
| **Africa** | 4.9 | 6.8 | 11.5 | 15.2 | 14.8 | 14.6 | 14.3 | 10.2 | 10.3 | 10.1 |
| Algeria | 0.3 | 0.4 | 51.4 | 50.2 | 0.2 | 0.2 | 0.0 | 0.1 | 0.0 | 0.0 |
| Angola | 1.2 | 6.0 | 6.5 | 6.5 | 19.1 | 16.1 | 4.4 | 2.6 | 33.5 | 27.3 |
| Benin | 1.4 | 5.2 | 1.7 | 3.0 | 21.0 | 20.0 | 6.8 | 6.8 | 24.2 | 21.8 |
| Botswana | 0.0 | 2.5 | 5.2 | 12.6 | 22.8 | 16.8 | 30.0 | 12.0 | 0.0 | 0.0 |
| Burkina Faso | 2.7 | 5.8 | 1.8 | 1.4 | 6.7 | 12.3 | 63.7 | 56.1 | 0.9 | 0.1 |
| Burundi | 0.3 | 1.8 | 1.4 | 2.0 | 13.8 | 12.3 | 2.0 | 3.7 | 9.3 | 9.5 |
| Cameroon | 1.4 | 4.8 | 2.9 | 6.1 | 20.0 | 14.3 | 15.8 | 13.0 | 9.4 | 13.0 |
| Central African Rep. | 1.3 | 1.9 | 1.9 | 3.9 | 7.0 | 9.0 | 7.1 | 3.8 | 41.9 | 26.0 |
| Chad | 2.7 | 4.8 | 1.5 | 3.2 | 1.1 | 2.4 | 53.8 | 35.3 | 4.7 | 8.7 |
| Congo | 1.8 | 3.8 | 7.3 | 13.5 | 1.6 | 4.5 | 0.0 | 0.0 | 49.7 | 35.1 |
| Côte d'Ivoire | 16.9 | 21.3 | 3.8 | 5.2 | 10.7 | 9.3 | 2.0 | 1.4 | 10.5 | 12.4 |
| Egypt | 12.4 | 9.6 | 29.9 | 36.4 | 19.9 | 17.3 | 3.3 | 1.1 | 0.0 | 0.0 |
| Ethiopia, PDR | 0.0 | 0.1 | 10.1 | 16.1 | 15.1 | 18.7 | 15.3 | 11.4 | 0.0 | 0.0 |
| Gabon | 2.4 | 6.9 | 5.9 | 9.8 | 6.4 | 8.6 | 0.0 | 0.0 | 20.7 | 11.1 |
| Gambia | 27.0 | 38.1 | 2.7 | 4.6 | 2.6 | 3.8 | 25.5 | 18.3 | 2.2 | 0.8 |
| Ghana | 2.8 | 5.3 | 2.6 | 4.1 | 13.2 | 15.0 | 6.5 | 5.4 | 17.0 | 26.0 |
| Guinea | 23.3 | 33.9 | 1.4 | 5.0 | 4.3 | 3.1 | 5.3 | 2.7 | 14.6 | 10.5 |
| Kenya | 0.7 | 2.1 | 3.9 | 5.8 | 45.4 | 40.4 | 6.4 | 1.4 | 5.6 | 4.4 |
| Lesotho | 0.0 | 0.5 | 23.9 | 16.4 | 42.0 | 56.4 | 14.7 | 2.9 | 0.0 | 0.0 |
| Liberia | 41.6 | 42.8 | 2.1 | 1.7 | 0.0 | 0.0 | 0.0 | 0.0 | 25.7 | 19.8 |
| Libyan Arab Jam. | 3.9 | 4.2 | 37.5 | 37.9 | 0.1 | 0.2 | 0.0 | 0.0 | 0.0 | 0.0 |
| Madagascar | 51.0 | 48.9 | 1.4 | 1.7 | 5.0 | 3.9 | 0.1 | 0.0 | 11.6 | 16.3 |
| Malawi | 0.8 | 1.4 | 1.5 | 0.3 | 64.7 | 67.5 | 2.5 | 0.7 | 0.4 | 1.4 |
| Mali | 8.4 | 12.7 | 0.9 | 1.8 | 5.6 | 8.6 | 50.4 | 48.8 | 0.9 | 1.0 |
| Mauritania | 6.5 | 17.6 | 4.8 | 30.0 | 1.3 | 0.6 | 33.8 | 6.9 | 0.0 | 0.0 |
| Mauritius | 29.1 | 22.5 | 23.5 | 21.7 | 1.2 | 0.4 | 0.0 | 0.0 | 0.0 | 0.0 |
| Morocco | 0.3 | 0.4 | 42.5 | 44.2 | 5.4 | 3.7 | 0.9 | 0.3 | 0.0 | 0.2 |
| Mozambique | 3.3 | 4.2 | 3.6 | 4.1 | 15.4 | 23.5 | 8.8 | 4.2 | 44.2 | 38.4 |
| Namibia | 0.0 | 0.0 | 6.7 | 6.0 | 17.2 | 16.9 | 12.8 | 10.9 | 0.0 | 0.0 |
| Niger | 2.7 | 4.7 | 0.7 | 3.4 | 0.3 | 0.3 | 70.8 | 65.9 | 5.6 | 3.0 |
| Nigeria | 1.5 | 8.8 | 1.6 | 1.7 | 6.8 | 5.2 | 31.6 | 22.4 | 12.7 | 15.4 |
| Rwanda | 0.3 | 0.7 | 0.7 | 1.1 | 5.2 | 7.0 | 12.3 | 10.3 | 12.1 | 8.2 |
| Senegal | 18.9 | 27.2 | 6.0 | 8.4 | 5.3 | 5.4 | 27.2 | 22.6 | 4.0 | 0.7 |
| Sierra Leone | 43.6 | 45.2 | 3.7 | 3.3 | 1.5 | 1.2 | 1.6 | 3.8 | 3.9 | 3.9 |
| Somalia | 3.9 | 7.6 | 5.8 | 8.6 | 16.2 | 23.5 | 16.3 | 15.4 | 0.9 | 0.9 |
| South Africa | 1.3 | 3.1 | 15.0 | 15.9 | 34.4 | 32.4 | 1.7 | 2.1 | 0.0 | 0.0 |
| Sudan | 0.3 | 0.7 | 7.5 | 18.4 | 0.5 | 1.0 | 46.6 | 38.4 | 1.2 | 0.0 |
| Swaziland | 0.1 | 3.6 | 0.2 | 26.4 | 33.4 | 11.7 | 1.2 | 0.0 | 0.0 | 0.0 |
| Togo | 2.3 | 5.0 | 2.1 | 6.6 | 19.6 | 22.0 | 13.0 | 14.0 | 29.9 | 19.0 |
| Tunisia | 0.1 | 0.3 | 53.9 | 52.0 | 0.0 | 0.0 | 0.4 | 0.1 | 0.0 | 0.0 |
| Uganda | 0.5 | 0.9 | 0.9 | 0.4 | 7.4 | 7.8 | 15.1 | 9.5 | 9.0 | 17.0 |
| United Rep. of Tanzania | 3.6 | 7.0 | 2.2 | 1.9 | 22.7 | 31.8 | 4.6 | 4.9 | 25.5 | 21.7 |
| Zaire | 2.8 | 3.4 | 1.9 | 1.8 | 8.2 | 9.5 | 0.7 | 0.7 | 53.1 | 54.0 |
| Zambia | 0.6 | 0.4 | 7.1 | 4.0 | 50.7 | 64.6 | 5.8 | 1.3 | 4.9 | 9.0 |
| Zimbabwe | 0.6 | 0.5 | 7.0 | 10.9 | 41.5 | 41.5 | 15.1 | 5.9 | 1.1 | 1.4 |
| **North and Central America** | 2.0 | 2.8 | 14.3 | 14.7 | 8.8 | 10.2 | 0.2 | 0.1 | 0.2 | 0.1 |
| Canada | 1.0 | 1.8 | 18.4 | 18.4 | 0.6 | 0.7 | 0.0 | 0.0 | 0.0 | 0.0 |

*(continued)*

(continued)                              TABLE 6

## SHARE OF MAIN CEREALS AND ROOTS IN TOTAL DIETARY ENERGY SUPPLY, 1969-71 AND 1990-92

| | Share in total DES | | | | | | | | | |
| | Rice | | Wheat | | Maize | | Sorghum and millet | | Cassava | |
| | 1969-71 | 1990-92 | 1969-71 | 1990-92 | 1969-71 | 1990-92 | 1969-71 | 1990-92 | 1969-71 | 1990-92 |
|---|---|---|---|---|---|---|---|---|---|---|
| | | | | | *(Percentage)* | | | | | |
| Costa Rica | 14.6 | 16.0 | 12.5 | 10.0 | 10.8 | 6.7 | 0.0 | 0.0 | 0.5 | 0.4 |
| Cuba | 17.0 | 14.2 | 19.9 | 17.6 | 0.0 | 0.0 | 0.0 | 0.0 | 1.9 | 1.7 |
| Dominican Rep. | 13.8 | 19.2 | 7.3 | 10.1 | 3.6 | 1.6 | 0.0 | 0.0 | 4.5 | 2.1 |
| El Salvador | 4.1 | 3.6 | 7.4 | 10.3 | 35.6 | 34.8 | 9.8 | 7.4 | 0.4 | 0.6 |
| Guatemala | 1.2 | 1.1 | 7.3 | 7.4 | 54.3 | 51.4 | 0.0 | 0.0 | 0.1 | 0.2 |
| Haiti | 5.4 | 16.2 | 3.6 | 13.8 | 20.0 | 7.4 | 13.6 | 3.0 | 3.5 | 3.9 |
| Honduras | 2.5 | 2.5 | 6.5 | 7.4 | 44.1 | 39.0 | 2.3 | 0.7 | 1.2 | 0.2 |
| Jamaica | 6.5 | 12.9 | 25.3 | 18.0 | 2.5 | 3.2 | 0.0 | 0.0 | 0.4 | 0.2 |
| Mexico | 1.8 | 1.3 | 9.8 | 9.5 | 41.6 | 35.0 | 0.0 | 0.0 | 0.1 | 0.0 |
| Nicaragua | 8.1 | 13.2 | 5.8 | 8.2 | 31.3 | 25.2 | 1.1 | 0.8 | 0.8 | 0.9 |
| Panama | 27.2 | 21.6 | 10.4 | 10.8 | 7.2 | 6.0 | 0.0 | 0.0 | 1.6 | 1.0 |
| Trinidad and Tobago | 14.1 | 13.0 | 27.5 | 24.8 | 1.1 | 1.2 | 0.0 | 0.0 | 0.3 | 0.1 |
| United States | 1.0 | 2.0 | 15.1 | 16.3 | 1.6 | 2.6 | 0.0 | 0.0 | 0.1 | 0.0 |
| **South America** | **10.9** | **11.8** | **15.4** | **14.7** | **7.8** | **8.1** | **0.0** | **0.0** | **5.8** | **3.2** |
| Argentina | 1.4 | 1.6 | 27.0 | 27.3 | 0.7 | 1.7 | 0.0 | 0.0 | 0.5 | 0.2 |
| Bolivia | 5.8 | 9.4 | 18.5 | 17.2 | 11.5 | 11.6 | 0.0 | 0.0 | 4.4 | 4.2 |
| Brazil | 16.0 | 14.8 | 10.4 | 11.3 | 8.0 | 8.1 | 0.0 | 0.0 | 9.3 | 4.2 |
| Chile | 2.5 | 2.8 | 41.9 | 38.4 | 1.5 | 1.1 | 0.0 | 0.0 | 0.0 | 0.0 |
| Colombia | 11.1 | 12.2 | 6.0 | 7.0 | 15.7 | 12.9 | 0.0 | 0.0 | 5.2 | 3.5 |
| Ecuador | 8.4 | 15.5 | 7.2 | 10.1 | 11.9 | 11.5 | 0.0 | 0.0 | 2.8 | 0.7 |
| Guyana | 28.0 | 32.1 | 17.1 | 20.6 | 0.2 | 0.1 | 0.0 | 0.0 | 0.1 | 0.0 |
| Paraguay | 3.8 | 3.2 | 10.6 | 12.3 | 16.1 | 8.6 | 0.0 | 0.0 | 15.6 | 14.3 |
| Peru | 12.5 | 19.1 | 16.1 | 17.0 | 8.4 | 5.7 | 0.0 | 0.0 | 3.1 | 1.9 |
| Suriname | 34.2 | 29.8 | 17.4 | 20.8 | 0.4 | 0.2 | 0.0 | 0.0 | 0.5 | 0.6 |
| Uruguay | 2.1 | 4.6 | 27.8 | 24.2 | 1.9 | 5.5 | 0.0 | 0.0 | 0.0 | 0.0 |
| Venezuela | 4.2 | 5.9 | 15.6 | 15.8 | 17.4 | 16.0 | 0.0 | 0.0 | 1.8 | 1.3 |
| **Asia** | **38.2** | **35.3** | **14.3** | **20.0** | **5.1** | **5.0** | **6.2** | **2.7** | **0.9** | **0.6** |
| Afghanistan | 7.8 | 9.0 | 51.9 | 52.3 | 14.8 | 9.3 | 0.7 | 0.7 | 0.0 | 0.0 |
| Bangladesh | 73.9 | 75.2 | 5.9 | 8.4 | 0.0 | 0.0 | 0.4 | 0.3 | 0.0 | 0.0 |
| Cambodia | 78.8 | 81.7 | 0.9 | 0.0 | 4.4 | 3.1 | 0.0 | 0.0 | 0.4 | 1.3 |
| China | 38.2 | 35.4 | 12.2 | 22.4 | 8.0 | 7.7 | 6.6 | 1.2 | 0.2 | 0.2 |
| Hong Kong | 30.6 | 20.3 | 9.7 | 10.6 | 4.1 | 2.3 | 0.0 | 0.0 | 0.6 | 0.2 |
| India | 33.2 | 32.5 | 15.0 | 19.2 | 3.4 | 2.8 | 13.0 | 8.4 | 1.0 | 0.6 |
| Indonesia | 56.4 | 56.8 | 1.5 | 3.3 | 5.9 | 5.7 | 0.0 | 0.0 | 7.7 | 4.5 |
| Iran, Islamic Rep. | 11.3 | 12.4 | 48.0 | 45.3 | 0.0 | 0.2 | 0.0 | 0.0 | 0.0 | 0.0 |
| Iraq | 8.9 | 14.1 | 45.8 | 44.2 | 0.1 | 0.0 | 0.0 | 0.0 | 0.0 | 0.0 |
| Israel | 2.1 | 2.2 | 33.4 | 29.1 | 0.2 | 0.2 | 0.0 | 0.0 | 0.0 | 0.0 |
| Japan | 34.8 | 23.7 | 11.4 | 11.3 | 1.6 | 4.6 | 0.0 | 0.0 | 0.0 | 0.0 |
| Jordan | 4.6 | 7.1 | 52.2 | 42.7 | 0.0 | 0.1 | 0.0 | 0.0 | 0.0 | 0.0 |
| Korea, Dem. People's Rep. | 36.2 | 38.6 | 7.0 | 5.9 | 19.6 | 17.6 | 1.6 | 0.5 | 0.0 | 0.0 |
| Korea, Rep. | 45.2 | 36.4 | 11.4 | 10.9 | 0.5 | 2.9 | 0.2 | 0.0 | 0.0 | 0.0 |
| Kuwait | 16.5 | 15.3 | 26.6 | 23.3 | 0.0 | 0.1 | 0.0 | 0.0 | 0.0 | 0.0 |
| Laos | 76.7 | 65.2 | 0.5 | 0.2 | 3.7 | 5.4 | 0.0 | 0.0 | 0.6 | 1.5 |
| Lebanon | 4.1 | 3.3 | 42.2 | 31.8 | 0.4 | 0.3 | 0.0 | 0.0 | 0.0 | 0.0 |
| Malaysia | 46.4 | 32.1 | 9.0 | 8.5 | 0.8 | 0.7 | 0.0 | 0.0 | 1.4 | 2.1 |
| Mongolia | 2.1 | 2.7 | 42.1 | 39.1 | 0.0 | 0.0 | 1.3 | 0.7 | 0.0 | 0.0 |
| Myanmar | 74.0 | 77.2 | 0.8 | 0.9 | 0.5 | 0.7 | 0.5 | 0.8 | 0.1 | 0.1 |
| Nepal | 39.1 | 37.5 | 7.9 | 13.9 | 28.9 | 21.2 | 4.2 | 4.2 | 0.0 | 0.0 |
| Pakistan | 13.4 | 6.4 | 44.2 | 46.2 | 3.2 | 2.2 | 3.6 | 0.8 | 0.0 | 0.0 |

*(continued)*

108

*(continued)*

**TABLE 6**

| SHARE OF MAIN CEREALS AND ROOTS IN TOTAL DIETARY ENERGY SUPPLY, 1969-71 AND 1990-92 | | | | | | | | | | |
|---|---|---|---|---|---|---|---|---|---|---|
| | Share in total DES | | | | | | | | | |
| | Rice | | Wheat | | Maize | | Sorghum and millet | | Cassava | |
| | 1969-71 | 1990-92 | 1969-71 | 1990-92 | 1969-71 | 1990-92 | 1969-71 | 1990-92 | 1969-71 | 1990-92 |
| | *(Percentage)* | | | | | | | | | |
| Philippines | 42.8 | 39.5 | 6.5 | 8.4 | 5.8 | 7.5 | 0.0 | 0.0 | 0.8 | 2.9 |
| Saudi Arabia | 13.4 | 7.0 | 20.3 | 29.5 | 0.4 | 0.1 | 19.1 | 4.6 | 0.0 | 0.0 |
| Sri Lanka | 43.0 | 42.3 | 11.4 | 14.2 | 0.5 | 1.5 | 0.5 | 0.1 | 2.6 | 1.8 |
| Syrian Arab Rep. | 2.8 | 3.0 | 50.2 | 49.3 | 0.0 | 0.5 | 0.4 | 0.0 | 0.0 | 0.0 |
| Thailand | 70.2 | 55.4 | 0.6 | 2.4 | 0.0 | 0.2 | 0.0 | 0.0 | 1.1 | 0.6 |
| Turkey | 1.5 | 1.6 | 43.8 | 43.5 | 2.6 | 3.6 | 0.0 | 0.0 | 0.0 | 0.0 |
| United Arab Emirates | 24.9 | 13.7 | 20.8 | 18.9 | 0.0 | 0.3 | 0.0 | 0.0 | 0.0 | 0.0 |
| Viet Nam | 69.0 | 69.1 | 5.3 | 1.3 | 2.4 | 2.3 | 0.0 | 0.0 | 2.4 | 3.7 |
| Yemen | 3.6 | 6.0 | 14.3 | 45.2 | 1.2 | 1.9 | 48.3 | 12.7 | 0.0 | 0.0 |
| **Europe** | **0.9** | **1.1** | **24.6** | **21.9** | **1.6** | **1.5** | **0.0** | **0.0** | **0.0** | **0.0** |
| Albania | 1.5 | 1.6 | 35.0 | 50.0 | 26.3 | 9.4 | 0.0 | 0.0 | 0.0 | 0.0 |
| Austria | 1.2 | 1.3 | 16.7 | 14.1 | 0.7 | 0.8 | 0.0 | 0.0 | 0.0 | 0.0 |
| Belgium/Luxembourg | 0.5 | 1.2 | 21.4 | 17.9 | 0.3 | 0.5 | 0.0 | 0.0 | 0.0 | 0.0 |
| Bulgaria | 1.1 | 1.0 | 44.7 | 39.4 | 1.8 | 0.3 | 0.0 | 0.0 | 0.0 | 0.0 |
| Czechoslovakia | 1.3 | 1.1 | 24.8 | 24.6 | 0.0 | 0.0 | 0.0 | 0.0 | 0.0 | 0.0 |
| Denmark | 0.5 | 0.8 | 12.1 | 13.1 | 0.4 | 2.0 | 0.0 | 0.0 | 0.0 | 0.0 |
| Finland | 1.0 | 1.4 | 15.1 | 14.5 | 0.0 | 0.0 | 0.0 | 0.0 | 0.0 | 0.0 |
| France | 0.7 | 1.0 | 21.4 | 19.1 | 0.3 | 2.5 | 0.0 | 0.0 | 0.0 | 0.0 |
| Germany | 0.5 | 0.7 | 14.6 | 14.4 | 0.7 | 1.4 | 0.0 | 0.0 | 0.0 | 0.0 |
| Greece | 1.6 | 1.3 | 35.9 | 26.8 | 0.2 | 0.4 | 0.0 | 0.0 | 0.0 | 0.1 |
| Hungary | 1.2 | 1.4 | 35.4 | 26.8 | 0.0 | 0.2 | 0.0 | 0.0 | 0.0 | 0.0 |
| Ireland | 0.3 | 0.5 | 24.0 | 22.1 | 0.8 | 2.6 | 0.0 | 0.0 | 0.0 | 0.0 |
| Italy | 1.1 | 1.4 | 36.3 | 29.9 | 1.1 | 0.7 | 0.0 | 0.0 | 0.0 | 0.0 |
| Netherlands | 1.0 | 1.1 | 17.6 | 14.4 | 0.6 | 0.6 | 0.0 | 0.0 | 0.0 | 0.0 |
| Norway | 0.5 | 0.8 | 19.3 | 21.9 | 0.1 | 0.2 | 0.0 | 0.0 | 0.0 | 0.0 |
| Poland | 0.6 | 0.3 | 21.1 | 24.4 | 0.0 | 0.0 | 0.0 | 0.0 | 0.0 | 0.0 |
| Portugal | 4.6 | 4.2 | 20.0 | 20.5 | 8.1 | 1.9 | 0.3 | 0.0 | 0.0 | 0.0 |
| Romania | 1.2 | 1.0 | 38.8 | 33.1 | 14.8 | 10.6 | 0.0 | 0.0 | 0.0 | 0.0 |
| Spain | 1.8 | 1.5 | 26.1 | 18.0 | 0.3 | 0.2 | 0.0 | 0.0 | 0.0 | 0.0 |
| Sweden | 0.5 | 1.6 | 15.1 | 15.8 | 0.4 | 0.6 | 0.0 | 0.0 | 0.0 | 0.0 |
| Switzerland | 0.6 | 1.5 | 19.8 | 18.4 | 0.1 | 0.3 | 0.0 | 0.1 | 0.0 | 0.0 |
| United Kingdom | 0.5 | 0.8 | 19.5 | 19.5 | 0.7 | 0.8 | 0.0 | 0.0 | 0.0 | 0.0 |
| Yugoslavia, SFR | 0.6 | 0.3 | 43.2 | 38.9 | 6.7 | 5.1 | 0.0 | 0.0 | 0.0 | 0.0 |
| **Oceania** | **1.3** | **3.9** | **20.4** | **15.8** | **0.5** | **0.9** | **0.0** | **0.0** | **0.3** | **0.3** |
| Australia | 0.6 | 2.1 | 22.9 | 17.2 | 0.6 | 1.0 | 0.0 | 0.0 | 0.0 | 0.0 |
| New Zealand | 0.4 | 1.2 | 18.0 | 17.6 | 0.2 | 1.0 | 0.0 | 0.0 | 0.0 | 0.0 |
| Papua New Guinea | 8.5 | 16.3 | 5.1 | 6.3 | 0.0 | 0.3 | 0.1 | 0.4 | 3.3 | 2.6 |
| **USSR** | **1.2** | **1.7** | **32.9** | **34.6** | **0.1** | **0.1** | **0.9** | **0.4** | **0.0** | **0.0** |

*109*

**TABLE 7**

## RELATIVE INADEQUACY OF FOOD SUPPLY IN DEVELOPING COUNTRIES, 1969-71, 1979-81 AND 1990-92

| | Relative inadequacy of food supply | | |
|---|---|---|---|
| | 1969-71 | 1979-81 | 1990-92 |
| | ................................(Percentage)................................ | | |
| **Africa** | **10.5** | **10.0** | **10.2** |
| Algeria | 17.8 | 2.9 | 1.6 |
| Angola | 11.7 | 10.1 | 19.6 |
| Benin | 10.3 | 9.3 | 4.3 |
| Botswana | 9.1 | 9.6 | 7.3 |
| Burkina Faso | 28.9 | 32.0 | 12.4 |
| Burundi | 13.2 | 15.2 | 17.6 |
| Cameroon | 7.4 | 6.7 | 13.3 |
| Central African Rep. | 6.9 | 8.0 | 25.5 |
| Chad | 12.1 | 32.9 | 25.0 |
| Congo | 12.9 | 9.0 | 9.2 |
| Côte d'Ivoire | 5.6 | 2.2 | 5.0 |
| Egypt | 5.7 | 1.5 | 0.9 |
| Ethiopia, PDR | 23.9 | 19.0 | 28.0 |
| Gabon | 11.8 | 7.3 | 5.7 |
| Gambia | 10.2 | 14.5 | 7.5 |
| Ghana | 9.4 | 17.8 | 12.0 |
| Guinea | 9.9 | 8.1 | 5.8 |
| Kenya | 8.8 | 9.3 | 15.1 |
| Lesotho | 16.6 | 9.7 | 10.0 |
| Liberia | 9.2 | 6.2 | 23.0 |
| Libyan Arab Jam. | 4.4 | 0.3 | 0.5 |
| Madagascar | 4.2 | 4.3 | 8.0 |
| Malawi | 6.4 | 7.5 | 16.4 |
| Mali | 14.5 | 23.9 | 9.5 |
| Mauritania | 19.0 | 13.2 | 4.4 |
| Mauritius | 8.3 | 4.4 | 4.0 |
| Morocco | 5.3 | 3.0 | 1.8 |
| Mozambique | 20.1 | 20.8 | 29.2 |
| Namibia | 10.0 | 9.4 | 9.6 |
| Niger | 16.5 | 9.4 | 10.4 |
| Nigeria | 6.1 | 15.6 | 11.1 |
| Rwanda | 9.5 | 8.3 | 14.5 |
| Senegal | 5.6 | 5.6 | 7.9 |
| Sierra Leone | 9.3 | 10.3 | 19.9 |
| Somalia | 23.2 | 20.4 | 35.1 |
| Sudan | 10.1 | 8.5 | 10.9 |
| Swaziland | 6.2 | 3.9 | 2.5 |
| Togo | 7.9 | 9.0 | 7.8 |
| Tunisia | 5.2 | 1.3 | 0.4 |
| Uganda | 7.4 | 10.6 | 8.5 |
| United Rep. of Tanzania | 24.1 | 7.7 | 11.1 |
| Zaire | 10.2 | 12.0 | 11.2 |
| Zambia | 9.3 | 9.4 | 13.3 |
| Zimbabwe | 9.6 | 8.6 | 12.4 |
| **North and Central America** | **5.1** | **2.9** | **3.2** |
| Costa Rica | 5.9 | 3.9 | 2.2 |
| Cuba | 3.1 | 1.9 | 1.7 |
| Dominican Rep. | 13.3 | 8.3 | 8.6 |
| El Salvador | 17.1 | 6.1 | 4.1 |
| Guatemala | 9.8 | 6.9 | 6.3 |
| Haiti | 21.3 | 17.1 | 32.4 |
| Honduras | 6.5 | 7.8 | 4.6 |

*(continued)*

(continued)

**TABLE 7**

| RELATIVE INADEQUACY OF FOOD SUPPLY IN DEVELOPING COUNTRIES, 1969-71, 1979-81 AND 1990-92 | | |
|---|---|---|
| | Relative inadequacy of food supply | | |
| | 1969-71 | 1979-81 | 1990-92 |
| | | (Percentage) | |
| Jamaica | 4.7 | 4.3 | 5.6 |
| Mexico | 3.0 | 1.3 | 1.4 |
| Nicaragua | 5.0 | 5.8 | 5.9 |
| Panama | 2.3 | 3.0 | 4.1 |
| Trinidad and Tobago | 2.9 | 0.7 | 2.1 |
| **South America** | **3.8** | **2.7** | **3.0** |
| Argentina | 0.7 | 0.8 | 1.6 |
| Bolivia | 13.5 | 10.7 | 11.9 |
| Brazil | 2.8 | 1.4 | 1.1 |
| Chile | 3.4 | 3.9 | 5.1 |
| Colombia | 10.9 | 5.3 | 3.9 |
| Ecuador | 8.5 | 6.1 | 4.1 |
| Guyana | 4.8 | 3.0 | 5.6 |
| Paraguay | 2.2 | 2.3 | 2.9 |
| Peru | 4.2 | 8.1 | 15.9 |
| Suriname | 7.7 | 5.7 | 4.9 |
| Uruguay | 0.5 | 0.9 | 1.5 |
| Venezuela | 6.1 | 3.1 | 4.6 |
| **Asia** | **10.7** | **7.2** | **3.9** |
| Afghanistan | 10.6 | 10.7 | 34.2 |
| Bangladesh | 5.0 | 9.9 | 8.8 |
| Cambodia | 2.4 | 17.6 | 7.1 |
| China | 14.4 | 7.9 | 3.5 |
| Hong Kong | 2.5 | 2.1 | 0.8 |
| India | 9.8 | 9.3 | 4.9 |
| Indonesia | 9.3 | 3.6 | 2.2 |
| Iran, Islamic Rep. | 8.3 | 1.7 | 1.2 |
| Iraq | 4.5 | 1.0 | 4.8 |
| Jordan | 2.1 | 0.9 | 0.5 |
| Korea, Dem. People's Rep. | 4.2 | 1.1 | 1.6 |
| Korea, Rep. | 0.3 | 0.1 | 0.1 |
| Kuwait | 1.3 | 0.4 | 4.1 |
| Laos | 7.2 | 4.0 | 5.6 |
| Lebanon | 6.7 | 3.0 | 0.8 |
| Malaysia | 2.8 | 1.7 | 1.1 |
| Mongolia | 5.2 | 3.6 | 8.4 |
| Myanmar | 9.0 | 4.6 | 2.3 |
| Nepal | 13.8 | 15.4 | 7.3 |
| Pakistan | 5.3 | 6.3 | 3.5 |
| Philippines | 17.7 | 5.6 | 4.5 |
| Saudi Arabia | 17.1 | 1.6 | 2.4 |
| Sri Lanka | 4.7 | 4.7 | 6.4 |
| Syrian Arab Rep. | 4.3 | 0.8 | 0.4 |
| Thailand | 7.0 | 7.8 | 6.5 |
| Turkey | 1.5 | 0.8 | 0.5 |
| United Arab Emirates | 0.8 | 0.7 | 0.6 |
| Viet Nam | 5.4 | 7.1 | 6.0 |
| Yemen | 16.9 | 9.7 | 5.6 |
| **Oceania** | | | |
| Papua New Guinea | 6.7 | 3.5 | 1.9 |
| **Developing regions** | **9.8** | **7.0** | **4.7** |

*111*

TABLE 8

## PREVALENCE OF UNDERNUTRITION IN CHILDREN UNDER FIVE IN DEVELOPING COUNTRIES

| | Prevalence | | | | Sample size | Survey year |
|---|---|---|---|---|---|---|
| | Underweight | Stunted | Wasted | Obese | | |
| | | | *(Percentage)* | | | |
| **Africa** | **28.3** | **36.4** | **7.4** | **...** | | |
| Algeria | 9.2 | 18.1 | 5.5 | ... | 5 284 | 1992 |
| Burkina Faso | 29.5 | 29.4 | 13.3 | ... | 4 172 | 1993 |
| Burundi[1] | 38.3 | ... | 5.6 | 1.2 | 1 930 | 1987 |
| Cameroon | 13.6 | 24.4 | 3.0 | ... | 2 357 | 1991 |
| Congo[2] | 23.9 | 27.6 | 5.5 | ... | 2 429 | 1987 |
| Côte d'Ivoire | 12.4 | 17.2 | 8.6 | ... | 1 947 | 1986 |
| Egypt[3] | 16.8 | 21.6 | 9.7 | 4.8 | 1 628 | 1995 |
| Ethiopia, PDR[2,4] | 47.7 | 64.2 | 8.0 | ... | 20 230 | 1992 |
| Ghana[5] | 27.4 | 26.0 | 11.4 | ... | 1 819 | 1994 |
| Kenya | 22.3 | 32.7 | 5.9 | ... | 4 753 | 1993 |
| Lesotho | 15.8 | 33.0 | 2.4 | ... | 4 687 | 1992 |
| Madagascar | 39.1 | 51.1 | 4.8 | ... | 4 225 | 1992 |
| Malawi | 27.2 | 48.7 | 5.4 | ... | 3 235 | 1992 |
| Mali[1] | 31.0 | 24.4 | 11.0 | 0.5 | 926 | 1987 |
| Mauritania | 47.6 | 56.9 | 15.8 | ... | 4 807 | 1991 |
| Mauritius | 23.9 | 21.5 | 16.2 | 5.6 | 2 430 | 1985 |
| Morocco | 9.0 | 22.6 | 2.3 | ... | 4 502 | 1992 |
| Namibia | 26.2 | 28.4 | 8.6 | ... | 2 430 | 1992 |
| Niger | 36.2 | 32.3 | 15.8 | ... | 3 847 | 1992 |
| Nigeria | 35.7 | 43.1 | 9.1 | ... | 5 565 | 1990 |
| Rwanda | 29.2 | 48.3 | 3.8 | ... | 4 363 | 1992 |
| Senegal | 20.1 | 21.7 | 8.7 | ... | 3 793 | 1993 |
| Sierra Leone | 28.7 | 34.7 | 8.5 | ... | 4 595 | 1990 |
| Sudan (north) | ... | ... | 12.5 | ... | 15 534 | 1987 |
| Swaziland[6] | 9.8 | 30.3 | 0.9 | ... | 4 791 | 1984 |
| Togo[5] | 24.4 | 29.6 | 5.3 | 2.5 | 1 396 | 1988 |
| Tunisia[1] | 10.4 | 18.2 | 3.1 | 3.8 | 2 023 | 1988 |
| Uganda | 23.3 | 44.5 | 1.9 | 2.4 | 3 790 | 1989 |
| United Rep. of Tanzania | 28.8 | 42.6 | 6.0 | ... | 6 097 | 1992 |
| Zambia | 25.1 | 39.6 | 5.1 | ... | 4 899 | 1992 |
| Zimbabwe[6] | 11.5 | 29.0 | 1.3 | 4.4 | 2 485 | 1988 |
| **North and Central America** | **19.2** | **34.4** | **4.1** | **...** | | |
| Costa Rica[7] | 2.3 | ... | ... | ... | 176 935 | 1992 |
| Cuba[8] | ... | ... | 0.9 | ... | ... | 1987 |
| Dominican Rep. | 10.4 | 19.4 | 1.1 | ... | 2 884 | 1991 |
| El Salvador[6] | 11.2 | 22.8 | 1.3 | ... | 3 483 | 1993 |
| Guatemala[1] | 33.5 | 57.9 | 1.4 | 2.6 | 2 229 | 1987 |
| Haiti[6] | 33.9 | 40.6 | 4.2 | ... | 967 | 1990 |
| Honduras | 19.3 | 39.4 | 1.5 | 1.8 | 6 166 | 1992 |
| Jamaica | 7.2 | 8.7 | 3.4 | ... | 860 | 1989 |
| Mexico[2,9] | 19.0 | 35.1 | 5.5 | ... | 12 391 | 1989 |
| Nicaragua | 11.9 | 23.7 | 1.9 | ... | 3 301 | 1993 |
| Panama | 6.1 | 9.9 | 2.7 | ... | 853 | 1992 |
| Trinidad and Tobago[1] | 6.9 | 5.0 | 3.8 | 3.3 | 842 | 1987 |
| **South America** | **7.8** | **16.1** | **1.9** | **...** | | |
| Argentina[7] | 1.9 | 4.7 | 1.1 | 7.3 | ... | ... |
| Bolivia[1] | 15.7 | 28.3 | 4.4 | ... | 2 698 | 1994 |
| Brazil | 7.0 | 15.4 | 2.0 | 5.4 | 7 314 | 1989 |
| Chile | 0.9 | 2.6 | 0.3 | 6.6 | 1 300 000 | 1994 |
| Colombia | 10.1 | 16.6 | 2.9 | ... | 1 973 | 1989 |
| Ecuador | 16.5 | 34.0 | 1.7 | ... | 7 798 | 1986 |

*(continued)*

112

*(continued)*

**TABLE 8**

## PREVALENCE OF UNDERNUTRITION IN CHILDREN UNDER FIVE IN DEVELOPING COUNTRIES

| | Prevalence | | | | Sample size | Survey year |
|---|---|---|---|---|---|---|
| | Underweight | Stunted | Wasted | Obese | | |
| | *(Percentage)* | | | | | |
| Guyana | 22.1 | 20.7 | 8.5 | 2.3 | 532 | 1981 |
| Peru | 10.8 | 36.5 | 1.4 | ... | 7 035 | 1992 |
| Paraguay | 3.7 | 16.6 | 0.3 | ... | 3 389 | 1990 |
| Uruguay[7] | 7.4 | 15.9 | ... | ... | 3 471 | 1987 |
| Venezuela | 10.2 | 6.4 | 1.3 | 3.3 | 6 745 | 1982 |
| **Asia** | **38.9** | **44.8** | **10.5** | **...** | | |
| Bangladesh[4] | 65.8 | 64.6 | 15.5 | 0.3 | 1 914 | 1990 |
| China | 17.4 | 31.4 | 3.4 | 4.3 | 6 329 | 1992 |
| India | 61.0 | 61.2 | 18.9 | ... | 2 948 | 1992 |
| Indonesia | 39.9 | ... | ... | ... | 28 169 | 1987 |
| Iraq | 11.9 | 21.8 | 3.4 | ... | 2 565 | 1991 |
| Jordan | 6.4 | 19.3 | 2.8 | ... | 6 601 | 1990 |
| Kuwait[7] | 6.4 | 12.2 | 2.6 | ... | 2 554 | 1984 |
| Laos | 40.0 | 47.3 | 10.5 | ... | 2 950 | 1994 |
| Malaysia | 23.3 | ... | ... | ... | 313 246 | 1993 |
| Mongolia[10] | 12.3 | 26.4 | 1.7 | ... | 1 679 | 1992 |
| Myanmar[5] | 36.7 | 40.0 | 11.2 | ... | 5 540 | 1991 |
| Pakistan | 40.4 | 50.0 | 9.2 | ... | 4 037 | 1991 |
| Philippines | 33.4 | 34.7 | 7.3 | 0.9 | 5 858 | 1992 |
| Sri Lanka[1] | 38.1 | 27.5 | 12.9 | 0.1 | 1 994 | 1987 |
| Thailand[1] | 25.8 | 22.4 | 5.7 | 1.3 | 1 856 | 1987 |
| Turkey | 10.4 | 20.5 | 2.9 | ... | 3 152 | 1993 |
| Viet Nam | 44.9 | 46.9 | 11.6 | ... | 37 764 | 1994 |
| Yemen | 30.0 | 44.1 | 12.7 | ... | ... | 1992 |
| **Oceania** | | | | | | |
| Papua New Guinea | 29.9 | 43.2 | 5.5 | 1.6 | 27 464 | 1983 |

[1] 3-36 months.
[2] Rural population only.
[3] 6-71 months.
[4] 6-59 months.
[5] 0-35 months.
[6] 3-59 months.
[7] 0-71 months.
[8] 0-11 months.
[9] 12-59 months.
[10] 0-47 months.

*Source:* WHO Global Database on Child Growth.

114

This appendix deals with the conceptual issues concerning the assessment of food adequacy and with the operational procedures employed in estimating the extent of food inadequacy in a population. The assessment of food inadequacy at the national level has often been undertaken by comparing the average per caput dietary energy supply (DES) figure taken from a country's food balance sheet with an estimate of the average per caput energy requirement. This approach provides a measure of inadequacy based on the assumption that the available food is distributed in proportion to individual requirements within the population, i.e. the distribution is equitable. This assumption is not supported by empirical evidence, the primary causes being national socio-economic factors. In most developing countries, even if the total amount of food available for human consumption exceeds the aggregated individual requirements, a part of the population may still have an inadequate consumption level while another part has a more than adequate level. In view of this, the method of simply comparing the national per caput food availability with the average per caput requirement has long been discontinued. Instead, a methodology is used that assesses the proportion of the population that has inadequate access to food.

The methodology is essentially similar to that adopted in *The Fifth World Food Survey* but includes a number of improvements and additions. This appendix attempts to provide a comprehensive account of the procedures employed: section 1 describes the basic concepts and principles of energy requirements used in assessing the adequacy of intakes; section 2 discusses the need to deal with aggregated data and provides statistical measures of the prevalence and intensity of food inadequacy; section 3 deals with the statistical database and operational procedures used in the computation of estimates for the developing countries; and section 4 highlights the distinguishing features of the present approach compared with that of *The Fifth World Food Survey*.

## 1. BASIC CONCEPTS AND PRINCIPLES OF ENERGY REQUIREMENTS FOR ASSESSING ADEQUACY OF INTAKES

The estimation of the prevalence of food inadequacy is feasible within a distributional framework where the principles of energy requirements are used in conjunction with the distribution of food availability or supply of a given population. In this context, it is necessary to take account of the fact that energy requirements depend on several factors. At the level of the individual, it is a relatively straightforward procedure to include the effects of age, sex, body size and physical activity. Until recently, however, there has been controversy regarding certain influences that are not so well understood – notably, the possibility of the metabolic efficiency of energy utilization in an individual varying systematically in response to changes in energy intake. Since the time of *The Fifth World Food Survey* the consensus has been that, even if such intra-individual variation does occur, its magnitude is small in comparison with that of other sources of variation (James and Schofield, 1990). The approach adopted for the present survey, therefore, is not to make any correction for such an effect but to assume that, if any such variation exists, it was taken into account along with the random sources of variance, such as short-term day-to-day changes, by averaging over a suitably long time so as to correspond to the "habitual" concept.

The human body requires dietary energy intake for its energy expenditure, the principal components of which are: i) the basal metabolic rate (BMR), i.e. the energy expended for the functioning of the organism when the individual is in a state of complete rest; ii) the energy needed for digesting and metabolizing food and storing tissues during growth; iii) the energy expended in physical activities, both productive work and non-work (leisure) activities. Some additional energy is required by children to allow for physical growth and by pregnant and lactating women for the deposition of foetal tissue and the secretion of milk.

An individual is considered to be in a steady state or in a state of energy balance if his or her total energy intake equals his or her total energy expenditure. The concept of a steady state or state of energy balance is notional – no one is ever in an absolutely steady state (FAO/WHO/UNU, 1985, p. 20).

However, while on a day-to-day basis there is often no fine matching between intake and expenditure, over a longer period an individual is (on average) expected to achieve an energy balance (James and Schofield, 1990, p. 39). In view of this, energy requirements are based on either the energy expenditures or the energy intakes of reference groups consisting of *healthy, active and well-nourished individuals.*

Earlier assessments of human energy requirements were based on the intakes of a reference group or population. However, the Joint FAO/WHO/UNU Expert Consultation on Energy and Protein Requirements, which met in 1981 (FAO/WHO/UNU, 1985), recommended the expenditure approach for adults and adolescents. Thus, it defined energy requirement as follows:

> "The energy requirement of an individual is the level of energy intake from food that will balance energy expenditure when the individual has a body size and composition, and level of physical activity, consistent with long-term good health; and that will allow for the maintenance of economically necessary and socially desirable physical activity. In children and pregnant or lactating women the energy requirement includes the energy needs associated with the deposition of tissues or the secretion of milk at rates consistent with good health."

Energy requirement is therefore defined as a function of two basic variables: physical health as expressed by body size (weight) and physical activity. The FAO/WHO/UNU report also recognized the existence of a *range of body weights* that are consistent with healthy individuals in any age-sex group. Similarly, there is a *range of physical activity levels* that may be considered to be economically necessary and socially as well as physiologically desirable. It therefore follows that there is a *range of energy requirements for individuals* in any given age-sex group.

The existence of this range creates a problem in identifying all the individuals whose energy intake may be deemed inadequate. Consider the group of individuals whose (habitual) intake lies within the range of energy requirements. While for the group as a whole the range of intakes and requirements coincide, and the average intake may also coincide with the average requirement, the intake of any particular individual may still fall short of his or her own requirements. In general, therefore, unless each person's ideal body size and physical activity level are known (which is seldom the case) so that his or her respective requirements within the range can be specified, it is not possible to know the true food adequacy status of individuals.

However, the problem is made more tractable by the capacity of individuals to adjust their intake in line with their requirements.

> "Most people have the ability to select their food intake in accordance with their energy requirement over the long-term, since it is believed that regulatory mechanisms operate to maintain a balance between energy intake and energy requirement over long periods of time" (FAO/WHO/UNU, 1985, p. 17-19).

This regulatory mechanism means it is safe to expect that, if there were no constraints in the choice of intake, the individuals with an intake falling within the range of requirements would tend to consume according to their needs and, as a result, they would all be meeting their respective requirements. In fact, the report's recommendation to take the average of the range of requirements as the average intake norm for the group as a whole is based precisely on this expectation. Thus it argues:

> "This implies that one would expect there to be a correlation between energy intake and energy requirement among individuals if sufficient food is available in the absence of interfering factors .... If self-selection is allowed to operate, it is to be expected that individuals will make selections according to energy need and the probability of inadequacy or excess will be low across the whole range [of requirements] .... If the average energy intake of a class were equal to the average

requirement of the class, almost all individuals would be at low risk because of processes regulating energy balance and the resultant correlation between intake and requirement" (FAO/WHO/UNU, 1985, p. 19).

Of course, in reality people do face constraints in meeting their requirements – otherwise the problem of food inadequacy would not exist! However, the argument made here is that, as the intake of this group is high enough to fall within a range of intakes associated with healthy and active individuals, it is reasonable to expect that the individuals within the group would be free enough to choose an intake according to their respective requirements[1] (i.e. the probability of intakes being close to requirements is high). As stated earlier, this expectation may not hold true in reality so some members may still be under some degree of constraint, but the essential point is that, on the whole, the group can be considered to be free enough to bring intakes close to requirements. As a result, these individuals can be said to be at a low risk of food inadequacy (or excess).

However, the same argument cannot be made for individuals whose intake falls below the range of requirements. The regulatory mechanism of adjusting intakes to requirements may still work to some extent but, since their intake is below the range of requirements, the capacity of these individuals to meet their requirements must evidently be considered to be hampered by constraints on food consumption. Therefore, such individuals must be considered to be at a high risk of food inadequacy. On the other hand, individuals whose intake lies above the range of requirements are also at a high risk – although in their case the risk is that of suffering from the harmful consequences of an excess intake (i.e. obesity).

It follows from the above that the range of requirements can be considered as a range of acceptable intakes. As a consequence, the entire population in a given age-sex group can be divided into three classes: i) individuals whose intake falls below the range of requirements and should therefore be considered to be at a high risk of food inadequacy; ii) individuals whose intake lies above the range of requirements and should therefore be considered to be at a high risk of excess; and iii) individuals whose intake falls within the range of requirements and can be therefore said to be at a low risk of both food inadequacy and food excess. The idea is expressed in Figure 1 which shows the probability of inadequacy and excess for intakes falling within and outside the range of energy requirements defined by $y_l$ and $y_h$.

118

---

[1] This implies that the variation in intake is systematically related to the variation in requirement, thus leading to the expectation of a high positive correlation between intake and requirement for the group of individuals with intakes falling within the range of requirements.

For intakes ranging between $y_l$ and $y_h$, the probability or risk of either inadequacy or excess is low – low enough to be "acceptable". Thus, individuals with an intake within this range can be considered to have adequate food. As the individuals whose intake falls below $y_l$ are at an unacceptably high risk of food inadequacy, they are the ones to be captured in an assessment of food inadequacy. Accordingly, the lower limit of the range of requirements, $y_l$, is accepted as the minimum dietary energy requirement or the cutoff point for identifying the set of people with inadequate access to food. This is the basic principle underlying the assessment of the prevalence of food inadequacy in this survey.

An exception to the above principle has been made with regard to children in age groups below ten years. Their cutoff points have not been set at the lower limit of the range of requirements but at a level that is close to the average requirement ($\mu_y$). Recall that the justification for adopting the lower limit lies in the expectation that, within the range of requirements, individual intakes are likely to be in close proximity of requirements. However, this expectation is more likely to exist among those individuals who have the ability to choose their intakes than among those whose choices are made for them by others within the consumption unit (e.g. household). Since children usually belong to the latter category, their risk of inadequacy or excess within the $y_l$ and $y_h$ range is not likely to be low. As a result, the use of the minimum value of the range of requirements as the cutoff point may lead to a serious underestimation of underfed children. The scope for such underestimation is reduced by using a cutoff point that is close to but below the average requirement.

119

**FIGURE 1**

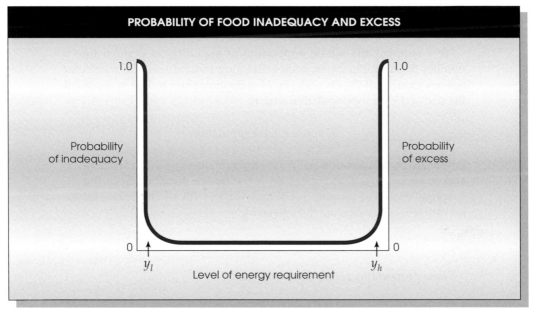

**PROBABILITY OF FOOD INADEQUACY AND EXCESS**

1.0                                                     1.0

Probability                                          Probability
of inadequacy                                        of excess

0 ↑                                              ↑ 0
$y_l$                                            $y_h$
Level of energy requirement

## 2. ASSESSMENT OF FOOD INADEQUACY AT THE NATIONAL LEVEL

This section explains the procedures for calculating the various measures of food inadequacy. First, however, it is necessary to address an issue of aggregation that is determined by the nature of the data available.

### The need for an aggregated distribution framework

It may be recalled that the cutoff point for identifying inadequately fed individuals is specified in the first instance for each age-sex group. If intake distribution data were available for each such group, the prevalence of food inadequacy could be estimated separately for each group and then added up to obtain a national estimate. In reality, however, nationally representative data sets on such age- and sex-specific intake distributions are not available. The information available is at best close to an aggregated distribution framework, i.e. the distribution of intake averaged over the different age-sex groups. As a consequence, a weighted average of the group-specific cutoff points must be applied. The link between this aggregated approach (applying a single cutoff point to a single intake distribution) and the disaggregated approach (first estimating the prevalence for each age-sex group separately and then building up the national estimate) is discussed below, as is the unit of analysis and classification in the aggregated distribution framework.

*The disaggregated distribution framework.* First, consider the case where the individual intake distribution for a particular age-sex group is known. If $y_l$ represents the cutoff point below which the intakes of individuals of the given age-sex group are considered to be inadequate, the proportion of the population with an inadequate intake is represented by $P_u$, the shaded area in Figure 2. Provided the necessary data are available, the computation of $P_u$ is fairly straightforward.

Now suppose the whole population of a country is divided into a number of subpopulations, each containing individuals of a particular age-sex group. Let $\Omega_1, \Omega_2 \ldots \Omega_M$ be $M$ subpopulations and let $n_j$ represent the size of the $j$th subpopulation so that:

$$\sum_{j=1} n_j = N = \text{total population}$$

Further, let $y_{lj}$ be the cutoff point for subpopulations $j = 1, 2 \ldots M$ and let $\mu_j$ and $\sigma_j^2$ be the mean and variance of the intake distribution of the $j$th subpopulation. The proportions of individuals with an inadequate intake for different subgroups are then given by:

$$(P_{u1}); (P_{u2}); \ldots \text{ and } (P_{uM})$$

These proportions are as shown in Figure 3.

The number of individuals with an inadequate intake in the whole population is given by:

$$N_u = P_{u1} \, n_1 + P_{u2} \, n_2 + \ldots + P_{uM} \, n_M$$

and the overall proportion of the population with an inadequate intake, i.e. $N_u/N$, can be expressed as the average of the respective subgroups' proportions, $P_{uj}$, with the respective population shares, $n_j/N$ where $j = 1, 2 \ldots M$, as weights. Thus, if the weighted average of one single individual from each of the M subgroups is defined as a hypothetical "average individual", $N_u/N$ can also be regarded as reflecting the proportion of underfed in a population composed of these "average individuals". This principle is utilized in the aggregated distribution approach.

*The aggregated distribution framework.* Suppose that the population is divided into M subpopulations corresponding to different age-sex groups, with the symbols $n_j$ and $\mu_{yj}$ denoting, respectively, the population size and the average energy requirement for group $j$. If $W_j = n_j/N$, the aggregated average energy requirement can be represented by:

$$\mu_y^* = \sum_{j=1}^{M} \mu_{yj} \cdot W_j$$

121

**FIGURE 2**

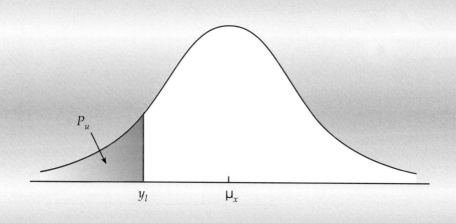

**PROPORTION OF POPULATION WITH AN INADEQUATE INTAKE, BASED ON KNOWN INTAKE DISTRIBUTION FOR A GIVEN AGE-SEX GROUP**

$P_u$

$y_l$

$\mu_x$

which is a weighted sum of the average energy requirements corresponding to the different age-sex groups. This is what is generally referred to as the average "per caput" requirement of a population. The aggregated cutoff point, which is derived as

$$y_1^* = \sum_{j=1}^{M} y_{1j} W_j$$

can similarly be referred to as the minimum per caput energy requirement. As both of these measures refer to weighted averages over the different age-sex groups, they can also be seen as referring to the minimum and average energy requirements, respectively, of the hypothetical average individual. The aggregated intake distribution can be formulated by considering the intakes of the subpopulations. Let $X_1$, $X_2 \ldots X_M$ represent the intakes of the $M$ subpopulations. The variable representing the aggregated intake is then given by:

$$X^* = \sum_{j=1}^{M} X_j W_j$$

and its mean and variance can be expressed as follows:

$$\mu_x^* = \sum_{j=1}^{M} W_j \mu_{xj}$$

$$\sigma_x^{*2} = \sum_{j=1}^{M} W_j^2 \sigma_{xj}^2 + 2 \sum_{j=1}^{M} \sum_{k>j}^{M} W_j W_k \, cov\,(X_j, X_k)$$

**FIGURE 3**

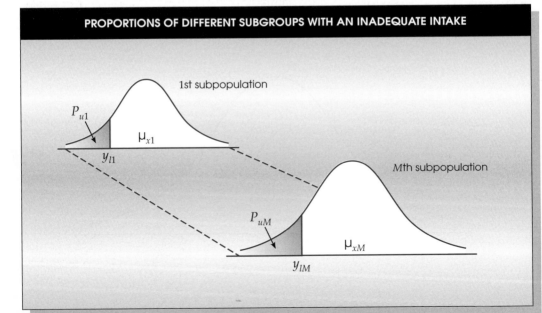

PROPORTIONS OF DIFFERENT SUBGROUPS WITH AN INADEQUATE INTAKE

122

The aggregated intake distribution $f(x^*)$ is not actually known. However, as will be discussed in section 3, it is quite plausible to assume that the distribution is log-normal and can therefore be approximated on the basis of estimates of the mean, $\mu_x^*$, and the variance $\sigma_x^{*2}$. Since $\mu_x^*$ is the weighted average of the group-specific average energy intake, it can be also expressed as:

$$\mu_x^* = \text{total energy intake} / \text{total population } (N)$$

which implies that it is given by the per caput DES figure from the food balance sheets. The estimation of $\sigma_x^{*2}$, which is a much more complex task, is taken up in section 3 in considerable detail.

Thus, in the aggregated intake distribution approach, the minimum per caput energy requirement, $y_1^*$, is used in conjunction with an approximation of $f(x^*)$ to determine the proportion of the population with an inadequate intake, $P_u^*$, as shown in Figure 4.

It is evident that, as in the cases of the minimum and average energy requirements mentioned above, $\mu_x^*$ and $\sigma_x^{*2}$ reflect the mean and the variance, respectively, of intakes expressed on the hypothetical average individual unit basis. This implies that, in the above aggregated distribution approach,

$$I^* = \sum_{j=1}^{M} W_j$$

**FIGURE 4**

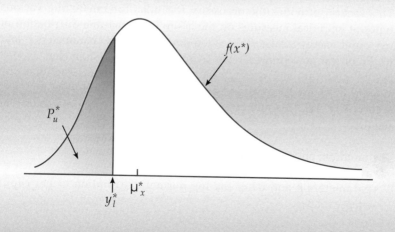

PROPORTION OF POPULATION WITH AN INADEQUATE INTAKE, BASED ON THE AGGREGATED INTAKE DISTRIBUTION APPROACH

which represents the hypothetical average individual, is the unit of analysis (and hence the units classified in the inadequate category) and the distribution is free from the effects of differences in intakes between individuals owing to age and sex. Since $I^*$ is equal to 1, it follows that:

$$NI^* = N$$
$$\text{and } P_u^* \simeq N_u/N$$

and hence:

$$NP_u^* \simeq N_u = P_{u1}n_1 + P_{u2}n_2 + \ldots + P_{uM}n_M$$

This means that the aggregated distribution approach is expected to provide approximations that are consistent with the estimates obtained by considering the individual age-sex-specific cutoff points and intake distributions separately. In addition, the extent to which the estimates based on the aggregated distribution approach can provide good approximations of the true proportion and number of individuals with an intake below their respective cutoff point depends on the accuracy of the approximated aggregated intake distribution, $f(x^*)$.

It is evident from the above exposition that, in the aggregated distribution framework, the population is assumed to be composed of $N$ hypothetical average individuals; the average individual, $I^*$, being defined as the average of one individual from each of the $M$ age-sex groups weighted by the respective population shares. In this way, the unit of the intake distribution is made consistent with the unit underlying the concepts of minimum and average per caput energy requirements. Hence, for convenience, the aggregated intake distribution is also referred to as the distribution of "per caput intake".

### Calculation of the prevalence and intensity of food inadequacy

This section provides the necessary formulae for calculating various types of empirical measures on the assumption that the distribution of per caput energy intake, $f(x^*)$, is log-normal with the parameters $\mu$ and $\sigma^2$. Empirical procedures for the estimation of these parameters as well as the minimum and average per caput energy requirements at the country level are discussed in Specification of the distribution of intake, section 3, p. 132. The numerical values of the following parameters are required:

- minimum per caput energy requirements, $y_l^*$;
- average per caput energy requirement, $\mu_y^*$;
- parameters $\mu$ and $\sigma^2$ of the log-normal distribution of per caput energy intake.

Having obtained the country-specific values for the above parameters, it is possible to provide analytical expressions for various measures of interest.

**Prevalence of food inadequacy.** The prevalence of inadequate access to food is measured using the probability that the average individual's intake will be less than $y_i^*$, which is given by:

$$P \text{ (inadequate)} = P_u^* = P\left[x^* < y_i^*\right] = \Phi\left(\frac{\ln y_i^* - \mu}{\sigma}\right)$$

where $\Phi(t)$ is the area under the standard normal curve to the left of the point $t$.

**Assessing the intensity of food inadequacy.** The intensity of food inadequacy indicates how far the access to food falls short of the desired level. It is measured from two perspectives, from that of the underfed, or undernourished, population and from that of the country as a whole.

*Assessing the intensity of food inadequacy in relation to the undernourished.* Two measures of the intensity of food inadequacy among the undernourished are discussed here: the absolute food deficit (or simply food deficit) and relative food inadequacy.

A simple measure of food deficit is derived by calculating the extra amount of energy needed to bring all the individuals whose intake is below the minimum requirement up to that level, a measure that is often computed in most empirical exercises. However, this measure underestimates the extra amount of energy needed to meet the requirements of all the people with an inadequate intake. This is because, as discussed earlier, the aggregate intake norm that will satisfy the requirements of all individuals in a group is given by the average and not the minimum requirement.

Suppose the per caput energy requirement follows a normal distribution with a mean of $\mu_y^*$ and variance of $\sigma_y^{*2}$. If the population size is $N$, then the total requirement of the population is given by $\mu_y^* N$. The total energy availability is given by $\mu_x^* N$. Now suppose there are $N_u$ individuals who have inadequate energy intakes and that the average intake of this group is denoted by $\mu_u$. The food deficit should then be defined as the extra amount of energy needed for the undernourished to meet their aggregated requirements. Since these individuals are from the same population, their requirements also follow a normal distribution with a mean of $\mu_y^*$. Therefore, their aggregated requirements would be given by $N_u \mu_y^*$. The total amount consumed is only $N_u \mu_u$; the total energy deficit or "total food deficit" would therefore be:

$$N_u \left(\mu_y^* - \mu_u\right)$$

The deficit expressed as a percentage of total energy availability ($\mu_x^* N$) is called the "relative inadequacy" of the current food availability and should therefore be represented as:

$$\frac{N_u \, (\mu_y^* - \mu_u)}{N\mu_x^*} = \frac{P_u^* \, (\mu_y^* - \mu_u)}{\mu_x^*}$$

The calculation of the above formula also requires a numerical value for the average intake of the undernourished ( $\mu_u$ ). This can be computed by taking the average of the intakes corresponding to the part of the distribution of $x^*$ below $y_1^*$, as follows:

$$\mu_u = \frac{\int\limits_{0}^{y_1^*} x^* f(x^*) \, dx^*}{\int\limits_{0}^{y_1^*} f(x^*) \, dx^*}$$

*Assessing the intensity of food inadequacy in relation to the country as a whole.* This measure indicates how much greater the per caput DES should be in order to reduce the prevalence of food inadequacy to a minimum or target level. The construction of this measure entails first estimating the required per caput DES level and then comparing it with the actual per caput DES. To estimate the required per caput DES level, two alternative strategies may be considered, reflecting two distinct assumptions about distribution: one assumes food supply growth with the existing inequality in distribution and the other takes into account the effect of a reduction in inequality to the fullest extent feasible. Since the more unequal the distribution is, the higher the required level of per caput DES would be, other things remaining the same, the two assumptions would lead to an upper and lower limit for the required level. Furthermore, by examining the implications that a full reduction in inequality would have for the prevalence of food inadequacy while keeping the per caput DES at the present level, it is also possible to see in which cases redistribution would suffice, in which cases growth would have to play the predominant role and in which cases a combination of the two would be needed.

*i) Growth with no change in distribution.* According to this strategy, the increase in food is assumed to trickle down to all households at the same rate, thus implying no change in the inequality measure as expressed by the coefficient of variation (CV). To derive the target per caput DES level, $\bar{x}_\tau$, the first step is to determine the mean of the intake distribution in the log scale ($\mu_\tau$) that will result in the targeted level for the proportion with an inadequate intake ($p_\tau$), on the assumption that the standard deviation (SD) in the log scale ($\sigma$) remains at the present level; and the second is to translate the resulting mean into the mean in the original scale.

The first step is undertaken by equating the normal deviate of the intake level at the cutoff point in the log scale to the standard normal deviate corresponding to the targeted percentage level, which can be expressed as follows:

$$(ln \ y_1^* - \mu_\tau)/\sigma = - z_{p\tau}$$

so that:

$$\mu_\tau = \sigma \, z_{p\tau} + ln \ y_1^*$$

The required per caput DES can then be obtained by using the following formula for the mean of the log-normal distribution in the original scale:

$$\bar{x}_\tau = \exp (\mu_\tau + \sigma^2/2) \qquad ❶$$

Increasing the average per caput energy intake without any change in the distribution of intake has the effect of shifting the intake distribution to the right, which reduces the proportion of population with deficient energy intakes but, at the same time, increases the proportion of population with excessive energy intakes.

*ii) Redistribution and growth.* In the preceding case, the inequality in distribution as measured by the CV is assumed to remain unchanged. As will be explained later, the CV is considered to vary between a minimum of 0.20 and a maximum of 0.35. Hence, when the CV is close to 0.20, the assumption of no change in the inequality of distribution is relevant. However, higher values, particularly if they are close to the upper limit of 0.35, imply that there is scope for reducing the prevalence of food inadequacy through redistribution programmes, for example by reducing the inequity in income distribution. Reducing the inequality parameter implies a higher share of the food supply growth for people with a low intake and hence a lower per caput DES target.

In view of this, it may be useful to consider the alternative strategy of first assessing the prevalence of food inadequacy on the basis of the current per caput DES and the minimum value for the inequality parameter in the log scale, $\sigma$. The resulting prevalence of food inadequacy would reflect the potential effect of a full decrease in inequality. If the prevalence estimate is still below the target level, then a growth in per caput DES becomes necessary. The target level of per caput DES in the above context is obtained by simply substituting the minimum value for $\sigma$ in Equation ❶ (above). The approach of considering the full effect of redistribution when calculating the required per caput DES level is attractive, since it represents the minimum per caput food supply that will be needed if the prevalence of food inadequacy has to be reduced to the chosen target level.

127

## 3. STATISTICAL FRAMEWORK FOR PRACTICAL ASSESSMENT

The basic theoretical underpinnings of the methodology for the assessment of food adequacy formed the core of the previous sections. This section focuses on the empirical procedures necessary to derive estimates of: i) the minimum and average per caput energy requirements; ii) average per caput energy intakes; and iii) a measure of variability in per caput energy intake expressed by the CV.

The estimation of these three vital elements is explained below; however, methods of estimation are necessarily conditioned by the type of data available and a few comments on the nature of the primary data are therefore offered, together with a few caveats that are necessary for a proper interpretation of the numerical results derived.

### Statistical database

As described earlier, the minimum and average per caput energy (calorie) requirements are derived by aggregating the lower-limit and average energy requirements estimated for individuals belonging to the different age-sex classes, using the age-sex composition of the population as a weight. Thus, the distribution of population by different age-sex groups is needed for each country. In addition, an estimate of the total number of births in any year is also necessary to derive the special energy needs of pregnancy and lactation. This information is essentially demographic in nature and the relevant data are available for most countries (UN, 1993). The age-sex-specific minimum and average energy requirements are derived on the basis of appropriate body weight and activity norms (see James and Schofield, 1990).

The average per caput energy (calorie) intake figures are based on national per caput dietary energy supply (DES) figures derived through the food balance sheet approach. The food balance sheets form an important component of the agricultural statistics system at FAO and are compiled using data from a variety of sources after close scrutiny for any inconsistencies. The data, which are available for most countries in the world, are the only major source of statistics for global food and nutrition studies.

However, the per caput DES figure from the food balance sheets, while reflecting the average food consumption level, does not necessarily provide an accurate measure of the actual energy consumption or intake level of a population, the principal reason being that it includes the food losses or wastage at the retail or kitchen/plate levels. A proper assessment of the actual intake level requires information from special surveys that measure the nutrition levels of households or individuals in a population, i.e. food consumption or dietary surveys. However, nationally representative surveys of this kind are costly and time-consuming to implement and have consequently been undertaken in very few countries. For this reason, FAO has to rely on the DES data while assessing the prevalence of food inadequacy in the developing world. Precise statistics on the extent of the bias resulting from the use of the per caput DES data in this context are not available. However, a study of household food wastage in the United Kingdom showed that wastage accounted for an average of 6.5 percent of the energy intake in summer and 5.4 percent in winter (Wenlock *et al.*, 1980). Since the percentages are likely to be lower in the developing countries, it may be assumed that the extent of the upward bias in the average intake level, as reflected by the per caput DES, is not likely to be large.

The per caput DES estimate needs to be supplemented by an estimate of the variance, $\sigma_x^{*2}$, to derive the distribution of per caput intake. A proper estimation of this variance also requires data on energy intakes of individuals classified by age-sex groups. Since such data are not available, the estimates have to be based on the only available sources of data pertaining to the distribution of food consumption within countries. These are the results of household expenditure surveys including data on food consumption and related variables. Household surveys provide data on household size and the total consumption of the households surveyed, thus leading to household-level data on per caput energy intake which can, in turn, be used as an approximation of the needed variance or CV of energy intake.[2] The household per caput variation, of course, does not refer to the equivalent units underlying the aggregated distribution framework discussed earlier. This unit, as indicated before, refers to the average individual with an age-sex composition defined as the weighted average of one person from each of the age-sex groups. The household per caput concept, on the other hand, while referring to an average of individuals in different age-sex groups, does not have a fixed age-sex composition, since this composition varies between households.

However, there is some empirical evidence to suggest that the variation in household per caput energy intake can provide a good approximation of $\sigma_x^{*2}$. Using detailed information on household intakes as well as the demographic characteristics of individual members of each household, an unpublished study on Tunisia found the SD of the logarithm of the household per caput intake to be about 1.0, while that of the household per consumer unit intake was about 0.8. As the consumer unit is also a standard unit with a fixed age-sex composition, this indicates that the household per caput variation provides a close approximation of the

---

[2] It may be noted that, in making this approximation, the intrahousehold variation referring to the differences between household members of different age-sex groups is ignored. This is precisely because, in the aggregate distribution framework, the unit of analysis is the average individual, i.e. a unit with a fixed age-sex composition. In other words, the distribution refers to units that are free from the effects of differences owing to age or sex.

variation between units that are free from the effects of differences in age-sex composition. A slightly different study of data from six regions covered by a Brazilian food consumption survey in 1974 showed that the contribution of differences in demographic factors in the variation of household per caput intake is relatively small.

It follows from the above that differences in body weight and activity levels and other socio-economic factors are likely to be the main contributors to the dispersion in household per caput energy intake. In view of this $\sigma_x^{*2}$ is approximated by the variation in household per caput energy intake while the difference between these two estimates is expected to be small.

### Minimum and average per caput energy requirements

As mentioned before, the minimum and average per caput energy requirements are obtained as the weighted average of the lower limit and average requirement, respectively, estimated for each age-sex group. It was also noted that the lower limit and the mean of the range of variation in energy requirements are in each case defined on the basis of the range of acceptable body weight and the range of acceptable activity norms. It is thus assumed that the energy requirements based on the combination of norms referring to a low body weight and light activity, on the one hand, and a heavy body weight and heavy activity, on the other, would reflect the range of variation in energy requirements for each age-sex group.

However, as explained in section 1, an exception to the above principle is made for children in age groups below ten years in the sense that the cutoff point or minimum energy requirement is set close to but below the average requirement. Thus, no allowance for variations in body weight is made and the norm is fixed at the median value of the range of weight for height given by the WHO reference curve. Similarly, the allowance for the effect of childhood infection for children below the age of two is taken as a fixed factor. However, the energy requirements per kilogram of body weight norms that are applied to the specified body weight include a 5 percent allowance to account for the fact that the energy intakes of the reference groups on which they were based do not reflect the optimum activity levels for children. This extra allowance is not included when defining the cutoff point. Therefore, the 5 percent extra allowance was excluded for the latter purpose but included for the purpose of the average requirement. Thus, the contribution of children below the age of ten to the minimum and average per caput requirement differed only with respect to the 5 percent extra allowance relating to activity.

As regards the adolescent and adult age-sex groups, the body weight for determining the lower limit of energy requirement is based on the lower limit of the range of acceptable weight for height, while activity is taken to be that corresponding to the light activity norms, i.e. 1.55 BMR for males and 1.56 BMR for females.

The body weight for the average requirement is determined on the basis of the median of the acceptable range of weight for height, and activity on the basis of the moderate activity norms, i.e. 1.78 BMR for males and 1.64 BMR for females.

However, the reference standard given by the New York Society of Actuaries for the range of acceptable weight for height was not considered to be applicable for populations in developing countries. Recent studies of the body mass index (BMI) have suggested that a BMI range of 18.5 to 25.0 is compatible with good health and physical functioning (Shetty and James in FAO, 1994b).[3] The range of acceptable weight for given heights implied by the BMI range has therefore been adopted in defining the weight norms for adults and adolescents. The median value of the range is 22.0. Hence, for a given height, the lower limit and the median of the implied range of weight for height are derived on the basis of a BMI of 18.5 and 22.0, respectively.

The extra allowance for pregnancy applied to females in the reproduction age groups is 100 kcal/day for the minimum requirement and 200 kcal/day for the average requirement. The average height figures needed for determining the body weight norms for all age-sex groups were obtained from the tables given by James and Schofield (1990). The body weight and activity specifications underlying the minimum and average per caput requirements are summarized in Table 1.

The procedures for calculating the respective per caput energy requirements on the basis of specified body weight and activity norms are described in detail by James and Schofield (1990).

---

[3] The BMI refers to weight (kg) divided by height² (m).

**TABLE 1**

| WEIGHT AND ACTIVITY SPECIFICATIONS FOR CALCULATING PER CAPUT ENERGY REQUIREMENTS | | |
|---|---|---|
| | Per caput energy requirement | |
| | Minimum | Average |
| **Body weight** | | |
| • Children (ages 0-9) | • Median value of weight for height range | • Same as minimum |
| • Adolescents and adults (ages 10+) | • BMI 18.5 and average height | • BMI 22.0 and given height |
| **Activity** | | |
| • Children (ages 0-9) | • Usual activity of children in affluent societies plus infection allowance for children up to two years of age | • Same as minimum plus 5 percent allowance for desirable activity |
| • Adolescents and adults (ages 10+) | • Males: 1.55 BMR  Females: 1.56 BMR | • Males: 1.78 BMR  Females: 1.64 BMR |

**Specification of the distribution of intake**

In order to derive the proportion of population with an inadequate intake it is necessary to specify the nature of the distribution of energy intake. While there is no direct information relating to the distribution of intake, on the basis of the average individual unit it is evident that such a distribution would be positively skewed. On the basis of the few household surveys providing data on the distribution of households by level of per caput dietary energy intake or consumption (from a wide range of countries such as Brazil, Egypt, Indonesia, the Republic of Korea, the Sudan, Thailand and Tunisia), three theoretical density functions were tested: the normal, the two-parameter log-normal and the beta distributions. The log-normal distribution was found to outperform the other two distributions in terms of the standard test for goodness of fit and, for this reason, it was chosen to represent the distribution of per caput dietary energy intakes.

The density function of the log-normal distribution is completely characterized by the two parameters $\mu$ and $\sigma^2$. If $\mu_x^*$ and $\sigma_x^{*2}$ denote, respectively, the mean and variance of the energy intake expressed on the "average individual" or per caput basis, then the four measures are related by the following two equations:

$$\sigma = \sqrt{ln \, (CV^2 + 1)}$$

$$\mu = ln \, \mu_x^* - \frac{\sigma^2}{2}$$

where $CV = \sigma_x^* / \mu_x^*$ is the CV of the per caput energy intake in a country.

Thus, the derivation of the log-normal distribution of intake for each country requires the estimation of the mean and the CV of energy intakes expressed on the average individual or per caput basis. The mean, as indicated earlier, is approximated by the per caput DES from the food balance sheets. Since the per caput DES is normally presented in terms of three-year averages, it excludes the effects of short-term random and seasonal variations and it is essential, therefore, that the CV also excludes these effects.

***Estimating the CV of energy intakes.*** It is important that the CV is measured accurately, as it represents the inequality in the distribution of energy intake. A low CV implies less inequality in the distribution and, unless the average intake is close to the cutoff point, a lower prevalence of inadequacy, and vice versa.

The procedures employed to derive estimates of the CV are designed to measure it as accurately as possible and to make sure that the estimates reflect only the variability in per caput energy intakes and not that of other factors influencing the survey data used for purposes of estimation.

*Relevant and irrelevant sources of variation.* The household consumption

132

data on which the estimate of CV is based are subject to variation owing to a variety of factors. It is therefore desirable to minimize the variability caused by factors other than the variability in energy intakes. The first factor in this process of minimization is the time frame. Since the per caput DES excludes the effects of short-term random and seasonal variations it has been recommended that the SD to be associated with it when deriving the distribution of household per caput calorie consumption should be standardized so as to reflect the consumption levels during a year. This recommendation arose from the consideration that most household surveys have tended to adopt the approach of distributing the sample equally and uniformly throughout the survey period (usually a year) and using a short reference period for data collection (a month, a week and sometimes even one day). In such a situation, the sample variance is expected to exaggerate the true variance for the survey period. In fact, the shorter the reference period, the larger the expected exaggeration.

There are, however, a number of other factors that tend to exaggerate the true variation, so it may be more appropriate to identify all the factors that are likely to contribute to this exaggeration and to distinguish between those that are relevant to the distribution of household per caput energy consumption and those that are not.

Following are the various sources of variation, classified into three groups.

*Group A. Demographic and physiological*
1. Household size
2. Body weight and height composition of individuals in household
3. Activity level of individuals in household

*Group B. Economic and social*
1. Income or purchasing power of household
2. Household preference
3. Local food accessibility

*Group C. Survey procedure and consumption concept*
1. Reference period of data collection at household level
2. Kitchen/plate wastage (if not excluded)
3. Food fed to pets (if not excluded)
4. Food given to guests or servants (if not excluded)
5. Measurement errors
6. Food eaten away from home (if not included)
7. Changes in household stocks (if not taken into account)

Since household consumption is expressed on a per caput basis, the effect of factor A1 (household size) is eliminated and only the remaining factors in Groups A and B are considered to be relevant. Therefore, every

133

effort is made to eliminate the variability introduced by factors in Group C. The influence of survey factors is minimized by standardizing the reference period of the survey at *one year*. The other irrelevant effects from Group C are minimized through the estimation of the CV or variance on the basis of the averages corresponding to groups of households rather than the individual household data. The various types of survey errors and the related variance may be cancelled out during the process of averaging for the groups. Such groups are formed on the basis of the per caput calorie consumption level; the adjustment procedures are described in the section Adjusting the CV to exclude irrelevant variations in household per caput consumption, p. 137.

*Methodologies for dealing with different data situations.* The number of countries with data on the distribution of household per caput calorie consumption has increased significantly since *The Fifth World Food Survey* owing to a special data acquisition programme carried out in 1990-91 in collaboration with national statistical organizations or nutrition institutes in selected countries; nevertheless, these data are still not available for the majority of countries. Consequently, the general strategy adopted is to make the maximum use of any available information that had a bearing on the variation of energy intake among households of each country. Since information availability varied from one country to another, the techniques utilized are also varied.

The countries were classified into the following five categories, arranged in descending order according to the amount of data available:

*Category A*
Countries for which, in addition to food balance sheets, household-level data were available on energy intake, food expenditure and total income or expenditure.

*Category B*
Countries for which data similar to those for Category A existed but where the energy intake data were given only for groups of households classified in terms of income or expenditure.

*Category C*
Countries for which no energy intake distribution data were available, even for groups of households but for which the rest of the information characterizing Category B was available.

*Category D*
Countries for which there were no data on the distribution of energy intake or food expenditure but for which data were available on income or total expenditure distribution.

134

*Category E*
Countries for which there were no data except food balance sheets.

For Category A countries, the CV could be calculated directly from household-level data on energy intakes while, for the other categories, recourse had to be made to indirect methods which became progressively more indirect as the data grew scarcer. For countries in Category E, there was virtually no satisfactory basis for estimating the distribution parameter; their CV was therefore set equal to the weighted average of the CVs for countries in their respective regions.

The basic approach for estimating the CV for countries in Categories B, C and D is essentially the same as that described in the Appendix of *The Fifth World Food Survey* (FAO, 1987). Therefore, only the key features are given here.

The estimation was based on two considerations: first, energy intake is positively correlated with income or with total expenditure, taken as a proxy for income; and second, in so far as the variation in energy intakes is influenced by factors other than income, it is necessary to increase the income-induced variation to account for the non-income factors.

For a given country, it is assumed that the household per caput calorie consumption can be linked to household per caput income (or total expenditure) by the following regression equation:

$$x_i = \alpha + \beta \ln V_i + e_i$$ ❷

where $x_i$ is the per caput calorie consumption for the $i$th household, $\ln V_i$ is the natural logarithm of the per caput income for the same household and $e_i$ is the error term reflecting the composite effect of non-income factors. Assuming that $e$ is independent of $V$, it follows that:

$$\sigma_x^2 = \beta^2 \, \sigma_{\ln V}^2 + \sigma_e^2$$
$$= \beta^2 \, \sigma_{\ln V}^2 / \gamma^2$$

where

$$\gamma^2 = 1 - \frac{\sigma_e^2}{\sigma_x^2}$$

The CV can then be formulated as:

$$CV(x) = \frac{\sigma_x}{\bar{x}} = \frac{\eta_x \sigma_{\ln V}}{\gamma}$$ ❸

where

$$\eta_x = \frac{\beta}{\bar{x}}$$

Here, $\eta_x$ is the income elasticity of household per caput calorie consumption taken at the mean household per caput consumption level, $\bar{x}$.

Thus, it may be noted from Equation ❸ (p. 135) that, given the value of $\sigma_{\ln V}$, as estimated from the available income distribution data, the CV can be estimated on the basis of assumptions or estimates for $\eta_x$ and $\gamma$. Since $\gamma$ is the coefficient of correlation between energy intake and income, a greater influence of non-income variables will imply a lower value of $\gamma$ and hence a higher value of the adjustment factor $1/\gamma$.

The value of $\sigma_{\ln V}$ can be estimated directly from survey data, since surveys for all countries in Categories A, B, C and D report household distribution of income or its proxy, total expenditure. The same, however, is not true for $\gamma$, since no bivariate household data on energy intake and income (or total expenditure) are available for Categories C and D and, for Category B, they are available only in grouped form which fails to reflect the true correlation between household energy intake and income. An equation to estimate $\gamma$ was therefore derived from the relevant household-level data available in the surveys of Category A countries.

This relationship was estimated for Category A countries through a regression analysis (cross-sectional), yielding the following empirical equation:

$$\gamma^2 = 0.114 + 3.28\, \eta_x^2 \qquad ❹$$

with $R^2 = 0.84$.

Using Equation ❸ (p. 135) and the calculated values of $\eta_x$, $\gamma$ and $\sigma_{\ln V}$, the CV of energy intake was estimated for each of the Category A countries and the observed CV was also calculated from the survey data; the difference was found to be slight in each case. Equation ❹ (above) was therefore used to estimate $\gamma$ for the countries in Categories B, C and D.

For countries in Category B, survey results were available for dietary energy intakes by income class, so $\eta_x$ could be estimated directly from the appropriate Engel's function fitted to the grouped data. In general, the semi-log form performed as well as or better than the other functions and it was therefore chosen for calculating the elasticities at the average intake level.

No data on the distribution of energy intake by income groups were available for the Category C countries but the food expenditure distributions were known. The latter enabled estimation of the elasticity of food expenditure ($\eta_f$) with respect to income. On the basis of this and an estimate of the ratio, $\eta_x/\eta_f$, $\eta_x$ was derived. The ratio $\eta_x/\eta_f$ was estimated through a regression equation linking it with the ratio of food expenditure to total expenditure.

Since food expenditure distributions were not available for the Category D countries, an indirect estimate of $\eta_f$ was obtained on the basis of an equation linking the elasticity for food expenditure with other socio-economic variables. The procedure for deriving $\eta_x$ was then the same as described above for the Category C countries.

It should be pointed out that the regression equations derived for the above-mentioned purpose of estimation reflect a pragmatic attempt to make full and effective use of all the available information from sources for all the countries (however incomplete these sources may be) in determining the CV of energy intakes for different countries. Their formulation has in fact been dictated by data availability rather than economically meaningful criteria. In view of this, their mechanical application, especially outside a certain range, is likely to lead to unacceptably high or low values for the estimated dependent variables and even the CV. This problem was, however, attenuated by the imposition of the 0.20 to 0.35 limits for the CV (see Adjusting the CV based on a sample distribution of household per caput calorie consumption [Category A countries], p. 140).

*Adjusting the CV to exclude irrelevant variations in household per caput consumption.* As mentioned earlier, the household consumption data from nationwide sample household surveys usually refer to a single reference period (a month, a week or, more rarely, one day) during a year; therefore, the estimated interhousehold CV is confounded by the within-year random and seasonal variations in a household's consumption. Furthermore, the survey design and methodology are rarely sufficiently precise to provide an unbiased estimate of actual household consumption during the reference period. In some cases, certain contributions to consumption are excluded; in others, consumption that should be excluded is included. Generally, household income and expenditure surveys have a questionnaire format that refers to food purchased or acquired during the reference period, making no distinction according to consumer, so food given to guests, visitors or tenants and food fed to pets and residual household wastage are included. Furthermore, food transfers to or from household stocks may not be adequately taken into account. Specialized food consumption or dietary surveys generally require the measurement of food consumed to be carried out by weighing the quantity of each food item prior to meal preparation as well as a record of the individuals partaking of the meals. In these cases, food eaten away from home is often excluded and the treatment of plate wastage varies. These measurement "errors" contribute substantially to the total mean square error.

It is the actual interhousehold average per caput variance relevant to the distribution that determines the estimate of the proportion below the cutoff energy adequacy level. It follows, therefore, that crude estimates of the CV based on a household survey with a single reference period need to be adjusted to allow for household variations and the non-sampling errors, as described above. As a basis for undertaking the adjustment, analyses of variance have been calculated for a limited number of data sets which allow the interhousehold and within-year components of the variance to be estimated.

137

*Magnitudes of the interhousehold and within-year variation in household per caput dietary energy consumption.* In order to assess the interhousehold and within-year variations, repeat measurements need to be made during the course of a year on a sample of households. The sets used derive from five subnational sample surveys of households, carried out by the International Food Policy Research Institute (IFPRI) in Bangladesh, Kenya, Pakistan, the Philippines and Zambia as part of a study on household food security, the nutritional impact of commercialization and food subsidies.[4] These surveys included repeat measurements, i.e. survey rounds, of the same sample of households over one year in order to reflect annual seasonal variations (see Table 2).

The analysis of variance was carried out on each of the above data sets by the Subcommittee on Nutrition (SCN) of the UN Administrative Committee on Coordination (ACC), in collaboration with IFPRI. The analysis provides the partitioning of the total variance into its between-round, interhousehold and residual components. Thus, if:

$x_{ij}$ represents the per caput calorie consumption for household $j$ in round $i$,

$\bar{x}_{.j}$ the mean over rounds of household $j$,

$\bar{x}_{i.}$ the mean over households of round $i$,

---

[4] IFPRI staff members responsible for the various country studies are: Eileen Kennedy (Kenya); Marito Garcia (Pakistan); Howarth Bouis (the Philippines); and Shubh Kumar (Bangladesh and Zambia). All are research fellows from the IFPRI Food Consumption and Nutrition Policy Division.

TABLE 2

| Country | Coverage | Sample size (No. of households) | Number of survey rounds | Reference period | Year of survey |
|---|---|---|---|---|---|
| **AREAS COVERED, SAMPLE SIZE, NUMBER OF ROUNDS AND REFERENCE PERIOD IN IFPRI HOUSEHOLD CONSUMPTION SURVEYS** | | | | | |
| Bangladesh | 8 villages in Comilla, Pabna, Khustia and Jessore | 301 | 3 | One day | 1982/83 |
| Kenya | Nyanza | 276 | 4 | One day | 1984/85 |
| Pakistan | Districts of Attock and Faisalabad (Punjab), Dir (North-West Frontier Province), Badin (Sind) and Mastung (Baluchistan) | 925 | 6 | One week | 1986/87 |
| Philippines | Bukidnon | 406 | 4 | One day | 1984/85 |
| Zambia | 10 villages in Eastern Province | 116 | 12 | One week | 1985/86 |

$\bar{x}$ the mean of the total data set,

$k$ the number of rounds, and

$l$ the number of households,

the analysis undertaken gives the format shown in Table 3.

The variances resulting from the round effect ($\sigma_r^2$), the household effect ($\sigma_h^2$) and the residual effect ($\sigma_{rh}^2$) need to be estimated on the basis of the related mean squares, as follows:

$$\sigma_r^2 = (M_r - M_{rh})/l$$

$$\sigma_h^2 = (M_h - M_{rh})/k$$

$$\sigma_{rh}^2 = M_{rh}$$

The total variance is given as:

$$\sigma^2 = \sigma_h^2 + \sigma_r^2 + \sigma_{rh}^2$$

The SDs and CVs of the total variance and its components for each of the five surveys are given in Table 4.

The interhousehold CV ($\sigma_h/\bar{x}$) ranges from 0.17 to 0.37. In earlier studies, an acceptable range for the CV corresponding to 0.20 to 0.35 has been suggested.[5] The results of these country studies tend to confirm the plausibility of this range.

The between-round effect CV, ($\sigma_r/\bar{x}$) ranges from 0.03 to 0.14. This represents the effect of seasonal variations for which an adjustment should be made if the estimated CV is based on single visit, single reference period surveys. The residual CV ($\sigma_{rh}/\bar{x}$) ranging from 0.25 to 0.38, incorporates the effect of within-year changes in household characteristics

---

[5] A likely range for the CV of household intakes was derived by considering the range of dietary energy intakes and the implicit SD in a hypothetical population composed of active and adequately fed individuals. Since, in such a population, individual intakes are expected to match individual requirements, the range and implicit SD of intakes can be estimated from the requirement distribution. Using this argument in a previous study (FAO, 1975), an estimate of the SD of intakes was given as 750 kcal on a consumer unit basis. This translates into an SD of 600 kcal on a per caput basis. However, this figure refers to the true intake or consumption level, whereas the per caput DES refers to food availability, i.e. the true intake and a wastage factor. This wastage factor is thought to increase the SD of the distribution up to a maximum of 10 percent, leading to an SD for the DES distribution of approximately 660 kcal. The per caput DES figure for different countries generally varies from 1 900 to 3 400 kcal. Using this range and the estimated SD, a CV range of 0.20 to 0.35 is derived.

(i.e. the true household × round effect) as well as the composite effect of the random variation and the measurement errors discussed earlier. An adjustment to the CV should be made for the latter but not the former.

*Adjusting the CV based on a sample distribution of household per caput calorie consumption (Category A countries).* The adjustment procedure for countries that have surveys providing data on a sample distribution of household per caput calorie consumption follows three steps:

- *Reducing the effect of the random variations and the measurement errors.* Since the effect of the random variation (being confounded by other interaction effects) is not quantifiable, the approach adopted is calculated to make a pragmatic reduction that should significantly reduce the effect of such random variations on the CV. This involves the derivation of the percentile distribution of household per caput dietary energy consumption, followed by the adoption of the median values of each decile group as the group value used for estimating the mean and the SD and, hence, the CV. Thus, random variations within a decile group (but not between groups) are removed.
- *Removing the seasonal variation.* The number and geographical spread of the country case-studies analysed are not sufficient to calculate precise country- or region-specific allowances for seasonal variations, so a single adjustment is made to the estimates derived for all countries. The country analyses indicate that a reduction of 0.05 in the CV is a reasonable global average adjustment.
- *Imposing an acceptable range.* The resulting CV value is then considered to confirm that it lies within the acceptable limits of 0.20 and 0.35. If it is still above 0.35, it is rejected and the CV is assumed to be 0.35. Similarly, if it is less than 0.20, the CV is assumed to be 0.20.

**TABLE 3**

| FORMAT OF ANALYSIS OF VARIANCE OF IFPRI HOUSEHOLD CONSUMPTION SURVEYS | | | |
|---|---|---|---|
| Sources of variation | Sums of squares | Df[1] | Mean squares |
| Between-round | $S_r = 1 \sum_{i=1}^{k} (\bar{x}_i. - \bar{x})^2$ | $k - 1$ | $M_r = S_r/(k-1)$ |
| Interhousehold | $S_h = k \sum_{j=1}^{l} (\bar{x}.j - \bar{x})^2$ | $l - 1$ | $M_h = S_h/(l-1)$ |
| Residual or error | $S_{rh} = \sum_{j=1}^{l} \sum_{i=1}^{k} (x_{ij} - \bar{x}_i. - \bar{x}.j + \bar{x})^2$ | $(k - 1)(l - 1)$ | $M_{rh} = S_{rh}/(k - 1)(l - 1)$ |

[1] Degree of freedom.

*Adjusting the CV based on income distribution data (Category B, C and D countries).* The household income or total expenditure data are also to a certain extent subject to the types of short-term random and seasonal variations discussed with respect to calorie consumption. Therefore, in considering the removal of these variations from the estimated CV, the consequences for all the three parameters ($\sigma_{ln(v)}$ $\eta_x$ and $\gamma$) on the right-hand side of Equation ❸ (p. 135) need to be taken into account. However, a precise assessment of the adjustments needed in each of these cases would require an appropriate analysis based on repeat measurements corresponding not only to calorie consumption but also to income (or total expenditure) on a sample of households. In the absence of such data, an approximative approach has been adopted in the present assessment.

For simplicity, it is assumed that the reduction in the variation of $x$ implies a reduction only in $\sigma_e^2$, i.e. the non-income component of the variation, so that the $\gamma$ value resulting from the fitting of Equation ❷ (p. 135) to the household-level data sets in Group A countries should be raised.

The adjusted $\gamma$ values for Group A countries (where the CV has already been independently adjusted) can be obtained by taking the ratio of the variance explained by income to the adjusted total variance. In terms of the corresponding CV values, this is equivalent to the following expression for $\gamma$:

$$\text{adjusted } \gamma = \eta_x \sigma_{lnv} / \text{adjusted CV}(x)$$

Thus, the use of the adjusted $\gamma$ values in calculating the regression Equation ❹ (p. 136) ensures the derivation of CV values that are to a

TABLE 4

### SDs AND CVs OF TOTAL VARIANCE IN IFPRI HOUSEHOLD CONSUMPTION SURVEYS

| Survey | SD | | | | Mean | | CV | | | |
|---|---|---|---|---|---|---|---|---|---|---|
| | Interhousehold | Between-round | Residual | Total | | | Interhousehold | Between-round | Residual | Total |
| | $(\sigma_h)$ | $(\sigma_r)$ | $(\sigma_{rh})$ | $(\sigma)$ | $(\bar{x})$ | | $(\sigma_h/\bar{x})$ | $(\sigma_r/\bar{x})$ | $(\sigma_{rh}/\bar{x})$ | $(\sigma/\bar{x})$ |
| | | | | | *(kcal per caput/day)* | | | | | |
| Bangladesh | 469 | 70 | 567 | 738 | 2 232 | | 0.21 | 0.03 | 0.25 | 0.33 |
| Kenya | 315 | 70 | 591 | 673 | 1 892 | | 0.17 | 0.04 | 0.31 | 0.35 |
| Pakistan | 611 | 316 | 873 | 1 107 | 2 280 | | 0.27 | 0.14 | 0.38 | 0.49 |
| Philippines | 487 | 73 | 565 | 750 | 1 855 | | 0.26 | 0.04 | 0.30 | 0.40 |
| Zambia | 808 | 177 | 697 | 1 081 | 2 172 | | 0.37 | 0.08 | 0.32 | 0.50 |

certain extent consistent with the definition adopted. In any event, as in the case of Group A countries, if the adjusted CV still falls outside the acceptable range of 0.20 to 0.35, it is either brought up to 0.20 or scaled down to 0.35.

For Group E countries where no distribution data are available, the procedure has been to adopt the weighted average of the CVs for the other countries in the region. In so far as the weighted averages are based on already adjusted CVs, no further adjustments are needed.

## 4. ESTIMATING THE PREVALENCE OF FOOD INADEQUACY: DIFFERENCES BETWEEN THE SIXTH AND FIFTH WORLD FOOD SURVEYS

This section briefly outlines the main differences between the approaches taken by the present and the previous survey in estimating the prevalence of inadequate intakes. The changes introduced in the present assessment refer principally to the problem of parameter specification rather than the basic methodological framework as adopted in *The Fifth World Food Survey*.

The principal changes introduced in *The Sixth World Food Survey* are summarized in Table 5.

**TABLE 5**

## COMPARISON OF PRINCIPAL ELEMENTS OF THE SIXTH AND FIFTH WORLD FOOD SURVEYS

| Elements involved | Sixth World Food Survey | Fifth World Food Survey |
|---|---|---|
| **A. Distribution of intake** | | |
| • Mean | Per caput DES from food balance sheets | Same |
| • CV | i) Defined to reflect the interhousehold variation in consumption during a year. Hence, CV is adjusted to remove the effect of short-term random and seasonal variations | i) Reference period undefined and hence CV taken as estimated from available survey data |
| | ii) Assumed to remain constan through the different time periods considered | ii) Same |
| | iii) Constrained not to be greater than 0.35 or less than 0.20 | iii) No constraint |
| • Shape of distribution | Log-normal | Same |
| **B. Cutoff point (minimum per caput energy requirement)** | | |
| • Reference body weight | i) For children, taken as the median of the range of acceptable weight for height | For children and adults and adolescents, taken as corresponding to the lower limit of the range of acceptable weight for height |
| | ii) For adults and adolescents, taken as the weight corresponding to a BMI of 18.5 and a given height | |
| • Activity allowance | i) For children, requirements reflect normal activity of healthy young children in affluent societies | i) Same, but including 5 percent increment to allow for insufficient activity among such children |
| | ii) For adults and adolescents, light activity with subsequent total requirement corresponding to 1.55 BMR for males and 1.56 BMR for females | ii) Absolute minimum activity with subsequent total requirement corresponding to 1.4 BMR (average for males and females) |
| • Intra-individual variation in energy requirement | Considered as immaterial after allowing for variation in body weight and activity and excluding short-term variations | Taken into account, thus leading to the application of two alternative cutoff points |
| • Allowance for infection among children | Included | Not included |
| • Changes in the age-sex distribution of the population over time | Taken into account | Not taken into account |

APPENDIX 4

# Anthropometric assessment of nutritional status

## 1. CHILD NUTRITIONAL STATUS
**Measurement issues**
**Data source: WHO Global Database on Child Growth**

## 2. ADULT NUTRITIONAL STATUS
**Body mass index**
**BMI cutoff points**
**Classification of nutritional status**

Nutritional anthropometry can be defined as measurements of the physical dimensions and gross composition of the human body as a means of assessing nutritional status. Some 20 years ago it was proposed that anthropometric measurements should be reported in relation to international reference values as a means of grouping and analysing anthropometric data and making comparisons across time and different population groups (Waterlow *et al.*, 1977).

## 1. CHILD NUTRITIONAL STATUS

### Measurement issues

The three most frequently used indicators of the nutritional status of children are based on weight and height measurements: weight for age, height for age and weight for height. The interpretation and transformation of these indicators for determining the prevalence of weight deficiency, stunting, wasting and obesity, and thus for classifying populations according to their degree of risk of under- and overnutrition, are described in detail in WHO (1995). Salient points that may assist the reader in interpretating the empirical evidence presented in Chapter 3 are presented here. In combination, these three indicators provide estimates of both current and past undernutrition or of current states of obesity. These indices alone do not provide insights into the underlying causes – in particular, whether the risk of malnutrition originates from food or non-food factors, or both.

Height for age and weight for height represent two different biological processes. Weight for height is sensitive to acute nutritional disturbances; a low weight for height is described as *wasting*. Wasting particularly tends to occur during the weaning period or in the second year of life, after which its prevalence tends to decline. Height for age is a measure of linear growth; a faltering of linear growth, or *stunting*, may occur as early as within three months after birth. The deficit in linear growth is difficult to reverse unless the child's environment changes for the better. Weight for age represents a convenient synthesis of these two processes. Because of the different distributions over time in children under the age of five, it has been recommended that prevalence data be disaggregated by age whenever possible.

The deviations of actual height and weight measurements from the corresponding age-specific median values in the reference population are converted into standard deviation scores (Z-scores) and a normalized distribution is thus generated for a population. In the case of the weight for height index, the deviations from the height-specific median reference values are normalized. The "normal" range on the normalized distribution for the three indices is taken to be between -2 standard deviation (SD) and +2 SD from the median (=0). The "low" range is then <-2 SD, and the "high" range is >+2 SD. On a population basis, therefore, the proportion of

145

children in the low, normal and high ranges of distribution can be estimated. In populations where a high percentage of children fall into the low range, children are said to face a high risk of being weight-deficient, stunted or wasted.

Data on weight and height indices are often aggregated for "children under five", as is done in Chapter 3. The application of the current NCHS/WHO reference standards for infants (0-12 months) has recently been questioned on the grounds that this is of limited value in assisting health and child care workers in the optimal nutritional management of infants (WHO, 1994). It has been recommended that a new reference be developed; however, insufficient data has been a limiting factor in developing such reference values for infants.

Debates have arisen in the past over whether national reference values for the comparison of nutritional status across populations should be established or whether a single international reference standard should suffice. It is now generally agreed that there should be a single set of reference values. Part of this argument is based on observations that the effect of ethnic differences on the growth of young children is small compared with the environmental effects. National or regional reference values, usually obtained from middle- or high-income groups, tend to differ little from the NCHS/WHO reference values, so the application of the latter in developing countries is likely to lead to few classification errors. Furthermore, national or regional reference values require constant updating, since developing countries are experiencing secular trends of increasing heights and weights. The costs and logistical problems associated with producing statistically valid national reference values are additional concerns. In view of all these considerations, for the time being WHO has decided to endorse the adoption of the NCHS reference values for international use until new international reference values can be developed (WHO, 1995). An international effort towards that end is currently under way (WHO, 1994).

### Data source: WHO Global Database on Child Growth

The estimates of the nutritional status of children under five presented in Chapter 3 were provided by the WHO Global Database on Child Growth. The current database includes prevalence figures from surveys in 131 countries, 100 of which have carried out national surveys. In most cases, the original data sets are reanalysed in collaboration with countries to standardize the information in terms of cutoff points, data presentation, reference data, etc. The criteria for the selection of surveys for inclusion in the database are: i) a clearly defined population-based sampling frame; ii) a probabilistic sampling procedure involving at least 400 children under five; iii) the use of appropriate equipment and standard measurement techniques; and iv) the presentation of results as Z-scores in relation to the NCHS/WHO reference population (de Onis *et al.*, 1993).

The surveys included in the current analysis were conducted from 1980 onwards, with two exceptions (Nepal and Liberia). For the purpose of estimating regional figures, these two cases were assumed not to have any relevant data. Almost two-thirds of the country surveys (44) included in the analysis were conducted between 1988 and 1993. The proportions of undernourished children obtained from these surveys were applied to the UN population figures for 1990 to estimate the number of undernourished children; 1990 represents the approximate mid-point of the period 1988-1993 (UN, 1993). This is also the procedure used by WHO itself in its own assessment of child undernutrition. Although the population figures refer to the number of children under five years of age, it should be noted that prevalence figures obtained from the surveys are not in all cases for children within this age group. Furthermore, WHO's classification of countries by region is not identical to FAO's classification.

The 73 countries for which survey data are presented accounted for 90.9 percent of all children under five in 1990 in the 98 developing countries for which estimates of child undernutrition are provided in this study. By FAO regions, these percentages are as follows: Latin America and the Caribbean, 99.9 percent; South Asia, 98 percent; East and Southeast Asia, 95.7 percent; sub-Saharan Africa, 79.5 percent; and the Near East and North Africa, 60.9 percent.

The following aggregation issues had to be addressed in order to arrive at regional and global estimates of underweight, stunted and wasted children: i) the estimation of the number of underweight, stunted and wasted children under five in countries where the survey covered an age group other than that of 0-59 months; ii) the estimation of the number of underweight, stunted and wasted children in countries which were not included in the WHO database; and iii) the choice of a procedure for the classification of countries for calculating regional and global totals.

The first of these issues was addressed by simply applying the proportion of children actually measured and found to be underweight, stunted or wasted to the estimate of the population under five. No adjustment was made to account for possible differences in the prevalence of undernutrition in different age groups within the population under five. In response to the second issue, that of deriving estimates for countries which had no survey data, the WHO methods were followed closely. First, the WHO regional classification was applied to classify the 73 countries. Next a weighted average prevalence of the three anthropometric indicators was calculated for each region and these average rates were then applied to the 1990 population estimates of children under five in the remaining 25 countries. This procedure thus provided an estimate of the number of underweight, stunted and wasted children in those countries. The third issue was then tackled by regrouping the 98 countries according to the FAO regional classification in order to calculate regional and global totals.

147

## 2. ADULT NUTRITIONAL STATUS

### Body mass index

Weight for height indices have long been used to assess the body composition of adults. Body composition is directly affected by nutritional risks. Different formulations of the height for weight index have been considered, the objective being to find an index that is highly correlated with weight and uncorrelated with height, i.e. interindividual variations should be due to differences in body weight as a proxy for body energy stores and muscle mass and not due to variations in height. The index of weight (kg) divided by height$^2$ (m) (body mass index [BMI]) has consistently been found to meet this criterion in different population groups. Other formulations have tended to be either correlated with height (e.g. weight/height) or to have a relatively lower correlation with body weight and a negative, albeit low, correlation with height (e.g. weight/height$^3$ or its inverse).

The BMI is an indicator of body composition. It has been shown to be related to body fat mass and to fat-free mass, the two main components of the body in addition to bone and water. Inter- and intraindividual variations in BMI are then due to differences or changes in body fat mass and fat-free mass. It has therefore been argued that a low BMI value represents a state of chronic energy deficiency (CED). BMI has also consistently been shown to be much less related to fat proportion, thus making it a valid indicator for both women and men. (Women normally have a larger fat proportion than men.)

Questions have arisen about the interpretation of BMI values in different populations. The relationship between BMI values and body energy stores appears to vary among different population groups in developing countries (Immink, Flores and Diaz, 1992; Norgan, 1990). Thus, a comparison across populations may be somewhat compromised but it can reasonably be argued that, in all populations, low BMI values indicate both reduced fat and fat-free mass. It has been found that a reduction in the latter mainly occurs at the expense of muscle (Soares *et al.*, 1991). This, in turn, indicates that CED is likely to impair physical performance. At the upper end of the BMI distribution, the relationship with body fat mass is consistently found to be strong, making the BMI a valid indicator for comparing the risk of various degrees of obesity across population groups. At the same time, weight and height measurements are easily obtained at a low cost and can easily be standardized to minimize measurement errors, while little transformation of data is required to construct the BMI. All these properties make the BMI an attractive index of adult under- and overnutrition.

### BMI cutoff points

The cutoff points applied to classify individuals and to obtain estimates of the proportion of the population at risk of being weight-deficient or obese were established by relating BMI values to various degrees of risk of morbidity in healthy reference populations. In a number of developed countries, the majority of adult women and men were found to have a BMI between 20.0 and 25.0, often referred to as the "normal" range of BMI. Optimal levels of BMI in women and men in developed countries are between 20.0 and 22.0, based on the association between life expectancy and the BMI. The lower limit to define CED in adults was obtained by taking the mean -2 SD of BMI distributions obtained from large samples of the United Kingdom's armed services personnel (both women and men), chosen as a provisional reference population because they were known to be fit and healthy. The lower limit, defined as above, turned out to be: 18.5 for men and 17.6 for women, as weighted means in both cases (James, Ferro-Luzzi and Waterlow, 1988). However, the common cutoff point of 18.5 BMI is now recommended for both men and women on the basis of existing evidence on the functional consequences of a low BMI.

There is some empirical evidence to show that a low BMI is associated with negative physiological, biological and socio-economic consequences. The suggestion is that aerobic work capacity is affected at BMI levels above 17.0 but that physical activity is not affected before this level is reached (Durnin, 1994). This is to be expected if low BMI values reflect reduced fat-free mass. Low BMIs in early pregnancy or prior to pregnancy among women in Egypt, Mexico, Kenya and Indonesia were found to be associated with low birth weights (Allen *et al.*, 1994; Kusin, Kardjati and Renqvist, 1994). Adults in Brazil with a BMI of less than 18.5 (or with a BMI greater than 30.0) were found to face a substantially greater risk of being ill than women with a BMI in the normal range (de Vasconcellos, 1994), and the same was found to be true for Rwandese women (Shetty and James in FAO, 1994b). Rural women in Kenya with a BMI of less than 18.5 spent as much time daily in work activities as women with a BMI of more than 18.5, although the latter group on average spent more energy per day (Kennedy and Garcia, 1994). Yet, Rwandese women with a BMI of less than 17.6 had lower average physical activity levels and more rest time each day than women with a BMI above this cutoff point (Shetty and James in FAO, 1994b).

The selection of 18.5 as the cutoff point to define CED in adult men and women may finally represent somewhat of a compromise (James and François, 1994). This cutoff point represents the third percentile among men with a median BMI of 23.0, and among women with a median BMI of 24.0, and a significant percent of overweight individuals may be included in the range of 20.0 to 25.0. With lower median values, for instance 20.0, the third percentile is 16.0 which clearly corresponds to high morbidity risks. Thus, the compromise for women and men in developing countries is to adopt 21.0 to 23.0 as the optimal range, and, as the normal range, 18.5 to 25.0 (James and François, 1994).

## Classification of nutritional status

Once weights and heights are measured in a given population, a BMI distribution can be generated for that population. By applying the cutoff points established in the reference population to this BMI distribution, estimates of the proportion of the population that can be said to be at risk of being chronically energy-deficient (<18.5) and the proportion at risk of being obese (≥25.0) can be obtained. The prevalence of adult CED in developed countries amounts to a small percentage. For example, 3 percent of men and 7 percent of women in France were found to have a BMI of less than 18.5 (Rolland-Cachera *et al.*, 1994). The invariable classification errors notwithstanding, the measured proportion of the population in developing countries with a BMI of less than 18.5 and equal to or greater than 25.0 is equated with the prevalence of CED and of overweight adults.

Risks of different degrees of CED are further indicated by dividing the area below 18.5 on the BMI distribution curve and applying the following cutoff points: 18.4 to 17.0, CED grade 1; 16.9 to 16.0, CED grade 2; and less than 16.0, CED grade 3. Equally, at the upper end of the BMI distribution, the degree of risk of obesity is indicated by applying the following cutoff points: 25.0 to 29.9, obesity grade 1; 30.0 to 39.9, obesity grade 2; and equal to or greater than 40.0, obesity grade 3.

# Bibliography

**ACC/SCN.** 1987. *First Report on the World Nutrition Situation.* Geneva, UN.

**ACC/SCN.** 1989. *Update on the nutrition situation, recent trends in nutrition in 33 countries.* Geneva, UN.

**ACC/SCN.** 1990. *Appropriate uses of anthropometric indices in children.* Geneva, UN.

**ACC/SCN.** 1992. *Second Report on the World Nutrition Situation.* Vol. I. *Global and Regional Results.* Vol. II. *Country Trends, Methods and Statistics.* Geneva, UN.

**ACC/SCN.** 1994. *Update on the nutrition situation.* Geneva, UN.

**Allen, L.H., Lung'aho, M.S., Shaheen, M., Harrison, G.G., Neumann, C. & Kirksey, A.** 1994. Maternal body mass index and pregnancy outcome in the Nutrition Collaborative Research Support Program. *Eur. J. Clin. Nutr.,* 48 (Suppl. 3): S68-S77.

**Delpeuch, F.** 1995. *L'obésité paradoxale dans les PED. Un nouveau défi pour les politiques de développement.* Paris, ORSTOM. (mimeo)

**de Onis, M., Monteiro, C., Akré, J. & Clugston, G.** 1993. The worldwide magnitude of protein-energy malnutrition: an overview from the WHO Global Database on Child Growth. *Bull. WHO,* 71(6): 703-712.

**de Vasconcellos, M.T.L.** 1994. Body mass index: its relationship with food consumption and socioeconomic variables in Brazil. *Eur. J. Clin. Nutr.,* 48 (Suppl. 3): S115-S123.

**Durnin, J.V.G.A.** 1994. Low body mass index, physical work capacity and physical activity levels. *Eur. J. Clin. Nutr.,* 48 (Suppl. 3): S39-S44.

**FAO.** 1975. *Population, food supply and agricultural development.* Rome.

**FAO.** 1977. *The Fourth World Food Survey.* Rome.

**FAO.** 1987. *The Fifth World Food Survey.* Rome.

**FAO.** 1993. *Compendium of food consumption statistics from household surveys in developing countries. Volume 1: Asia.* FAO Economic and Social Development Paper No. 116/1. Rome.

**FAO.** 1994a. *Compendium of food consumption statistics from household surveys in developing countries. Volume 2: Africa, Latin America and Oceania.* FAO Economic and Social Development Paper No. 116/2. Rome.

**FAO.** 1994b. *Body mass index, a measure of chronic energy deficiency in adults.* FAO Food and Nutrition Paper No. 56. Rome.

**FAO/WHO.** 1992. *Nutrition and development – a global assessment.* Rome, FAO.

**FAO/WHO/UNU.** 1985. *Energy and protein requirements.* Report of a Joint FAO/WHO/UNU Expert Consultation. WHO Technical Report Series No. 724. Geneva, WHO.

**Ferro-Luzzi, A., Shetty, P.S., Franklin, M. & James, W.P.T.** 1992. A simplified approach to assessing adult energy deficiency. *Eur. J. Clin. Nutr.,* 46: 173-186.

**Garcia, M. & Kennedy, E.** 1994. Assessing the linkages between low body mass index and morbidity in adults: evidence from four developing countries. *Eur. J. Clin. Nutr.,* 48 (Suppl. 3): S90-S97.

**Gibson, R.S.** 1990. *Principles of nutritional assessment.* Oxford, UK, Oxford University Press.

**Healy, M.J.R.** 1989. Nutritional adaptation and variability, three commentaries on the paper by Professor P. V. Sukhatme. *Eur. J. Clin. Nutr.,* 43: 203-210.

**Immink, M.D.C., Flores, R. & Diaz, E.O.** 1992. Body mass index, body composition and the chronic energy deficiency classification of rural adult populations in Guatemala. *Eur. J. Clin. Nutr.,* 46(6): 419-427.

**James, W.P.T. & François, P.** 1994. The choice of cutoff point for distinguishing normal body weights from underweight or chronic energy deficiency in adults. *Eur. J. Clin. Nutr.,* 48 (Suppl. 3): S179-S184.

**James, W.P.T. & Schofield, E.C.** 1990. *Human energy requirements.* Oxford, UK, Oxford Medical Publications, Oxford University Press.

**James, W.P.T., Ferro-Luzzi, A. & Waterlow, J.C.** 1988. Definition of chronic energy deficiency in adults. *Eur. J. Clin. Nutr.,* 42: 969-981.

**Kennedy, E. & Garcia, M.** 1994. Body mass index and economic productivity. *Eur. J. Clin. Nutr.,* 48 (Suppl. 3): S45-S55.

**Kurz, K.M. & Johnson-Welch, C.** 1994. *The nutrition and lives of adolescents in developing countries.* Washington, DC, International Center for Research on Women.

**Kusin, J.A., Kardjati, S. & Renqvist, U.H.** 1994. Maternal body mass index: the functional significance during reproduction. *Eur. J. Clin. Nutr.,* 48 (Suppl. 3): S56-S67.

**Norgan, N.G.** 1990. Body mass index and body energy stores in developing countries. *Eur. J. Clin. Nutr.,* 44 (Suppl. 1): S79-S84.

**Norgan, N.G.** 1994. Population differences in body composition in relation to the body mass index. *Eur. J. Clin. Nutr.,* 48 (Suppl. 3): S10-S27.

**Rolland-Cachera, M.F., Cole, T.J., Sempé, M., Tichet, J., Rossignol, C. & Charraud, A.** 1994. Body mass index variations: centiles from birth to 87 years. *Eur. J. Clin. Nutr.,* 45: 13-21.

**Soares, M.J., Piers, S., Shetty, P.S., Robinson, S., Jackson, A.A. & Waterlow, J.C.** 1991. Basal metabolic rate, body composition and whole-body protein turnover in Indian men with differing nutritional status. *Clin. Sci.,* 81: 419-425.

**Sukhatme, P.V.** 1982. Poverty and malnutrition. *In* P.V. Sukhatme, ed. *Newer concepts in nutrition and their implications for policy.* Pune, Maharashtra, India, Association for the Cultivation of Science.

152

**Sukhatme, P.V.** 1989. Nutritional adaptation and variability. *Eur. J. Clin. Nutr.,* 43: 75-87.

**Sukhatme, P.V. & Margen, S.** 1982. Autoregulatory homeostatic nature of energy balance. *Am. J. Clin. Nutr.,* 35: 355-365.

**UN.** 1993. *World population prospects. The 1992 revision.* Department for Economic and Social Information and Policy Analysis. ST/ESA/SER.A/135. New York.

**UNDP.** 1995. *Human Development Report 1995.* New York, Oxford University Press.

**Waterlow, J.C.** 1989a. Nutritional adaptation and variability, three commentaries on the paper by Professor P.V. Sukhatme. *Eur. J. Clin. Nutr.,* 43: 203-210.

**Waterlow, J.C.** 1989b. Observation on FAO's methodology for estimating the incidence of undernutrition. (UNU) *Food Nutr. Bull.,* II(2): 8-12.

**Waterlow, J.C., Buzina, R., Keller, W., Lane, J.M., Nichaman, M.Z. & Tanner, J.M.** 1977. The presentation and use of height and weight data for comparing the nutritional status of groups of children under the age of 10 years. *Bull. World Health Organ.,* 55: 489-498.

**Wenlock, R.W., Buss, D.H., Derry, B.J. & Dixon, E.J.** 1980. Household food wastage in Britain. *Br. J. Nutr.,* 43: 53-70.

**WHO.** 1983. *Measuring change in nutritional status. Guidelines for assessing the nutritional impact of supplementary feeding programmes for vulnerable groups.* Geneva.

**WHO.** 1986. Use and interpretation of anthropometric indicators of nutritional status. *Bull. World Health Organ.,* 64: 929-941.

**WHO.** 1994. *An evaluation of infant growth.* WHO Working Group on Infant Growth. WHO/NUT/94.8. Geneva.

**WHO.** 1995. *Physical status: the use and interpretation of anthropometry.* WHO Technical Report Series No. 854. Geneva.

1/5/96

**• ANGOLA**
Empresa Nacional do Disco e de
Publicações, ENDIPU-U.E.E.
Rua Cirilo da Conceição Silva, N° 7
C.P. N° 1314-C
Luanda

**• ARGENTINA**
Librería Agropecuaria
Pasteur 743
1028 Buenos Aires
Oficina del Libro Internacional
Alberti 40
1082 Buenos Aires

**• AUSTRALIA**
Hunter Publications
P.O. Box 404
Abbotsford, Vic. 3067

**• AUSTRIA**
Gerold Buch & Co.
Weihburggasse 26
1010 Vienna

**• BANGLADESH**
Association of Development
Agencies in Bangladesh
House No. 1/3, Block F, Lalmatia
Dhaka 1207

**• BELGIQUE**
M.J. De Lannoy
202, avenue du Roi
1060 Bruxelles
CCP 000-0808993-13

**• BOLIVIA**
Los Amigos del Libro
Perú 3712, Casilla 450
Cochabamba;
Mercado 1315, La Paz

**• BOTSWANA**
Botsalo Books (Pty) Ltd
P.O. Box 1532
Gaborone

**• BRAZIL**
Fundação Getúlio Vargas
Praia do Botafogo 190, C.P. 9052
Rio de Janeiro
Núcleo Editora da
Universidade Federal Fluminense
Rua Miguel de Frias 9
Icaraí-Niterói
24 220-000 Rio de Janeiro
Editora da Universidade Federal
do Rio Grande do Sul
Av. João Pessoa 415
Bairro Cidade Baixa
90 040-000 Porto Alegre/RS
Book Master Livraria
Rua do Catete 311 lj. 118/119
20031-001 Catete
Rio de Janeiro

**• CANADA**
Le Diffuseur Gilles Vermette Inc.
C.P. 85, 151, av. de Mortagne
Boucherville, Québec J4B 5E6
UNIPUB
4611/F Assembly Drive
Lanham MD 20706-4391 (USA)
Toll-free 800 233-0504 (Canada)

**• CHILE**
Librería - Oficina Regional FAO
Calle Bandera 150, 8° Piso
Casilla 10095, Santiago-Centro
Tel. 699 1005
Fax 696 1121/696 1124
Universitaria Textolibros Ltda.
Avda. L. Bernardo O'Higgins 1050
Santiago

**• COLOMBIA**
Banco Ganadero
Revista Carta Ganadera
Carrera 9ª N° 72-21, Piso 5
Bogotá D.E.
Tel. 217 0100

**• CONGO**
Office national des librairies populaires
B.P. 577
Brazzaville

**• COSTA RICA**
Librería Lehmann S.A.
Av. Central
Apartado 10011
San José

**• CÔTE D'IVOIRE**
CEDA
04 B.P. 541
Abidjan 04

**• CUBA**
Ediciones Cubanas, Empresa de
Comercio Exterior de Publicaciones
Obispo 461, Apartado 605
La Habana

**• CZECH REPUBLIC**
Artia Pegas Press Ltd
Import of Periodicals
Palác Metro, P.O. Box 825
Národní 25, 111 21 Praha 1

**• DENMARK**
Munksgaard, Book and
Subscription Service
P.O. Box 2148
DK 1016 Copenhagen K.
Tel. 4533128570
Fax 4533129387

**• DOMINICAN REPUBLIC**
CUESTA - Centro del libro
Av. 27 de Febrero, esq. A. Lincoln
Centro Comercial Nacional
Apartado 1241
Santo Domingo

**• ECUADOR**
Libri Mundi, Librería Internacional
Juan León Mera 851
Apartado Postal 3029
Quito

**• EGYPT**
The Middle East Observer
41 Sherif Street
Cairo

**• ESPAÑA**
Mundi Prensa Libros S.A.
Castelló 37
28001 Madrid
Tel. 431 3399
Fax 575 3998
Librería Agrícola
Fernando VI 2
28004 Madrid
Librería Internacional AEDOS
Consejo de Ciento 391
08009 Barcelona
Tel. 301 8615
Fax 317 0141
Llibreria de la Generalitat
de Catalunya
Rambla dels Estudis 118
(Palau Moja)
08002 Barcelona
Tel. (93) 302 6462
Fax (93) 302 1299

**• FINLAND**
Akateeminen Kirjakauppa
P.O. Box 218
SF-00381 Helsinki

**• FRANCE**
Lavoisier
14, rue de Provigny
94236 Cachan Cedex
Editions A. Pedone
13, rue Soufflot
75005 Paris
Librairie du Commerce International
24, boulevard de l'Hôpital
75005 Paris

**• GERMANY**
Alexander Horn Internationale
Buchhandlung
Kirchgasse 22, Postfach 3340
D-65185 Wiesbaden
Uno Verlag
Poppelsdorfer Allee 55
D-53115 Bonn 1
S. Toeche-Mittler GmbH
Versandbuchhandlung
Hindenburgstrasse 33
D-64295 Darmstadt

**• GHANA**
SEDCO Publishing Ltd
Sedco House, Tabon Street
Off Ring Road Central, North Ridge
P.O. Box 2051
Accra

**• GUYANA**
Guyana National Trading
Corporation Ltd
45-47 Water Street, P.O. Box 308
Georgetown

**• HAÏTI**
Librairie «A la Caravelle»
26, rue Bonne Foi, B.P. 111
Port-au-Prince

**• HONDURAS**
Escuela Agrícola Panamericana,
Librería RTAC
El Zamorano, Apartado 93
Tegucigalpa
Oficina de la Escuela Agrícola
Panamericana en Tegucigalpa
Blvd. Morazán, Apts. Glapson
Apartado 93
Tegucigalpa

**• HUNGARY**
Librotrade Kft.
P.O. Box 126
H-1656 Budapest

**• INDIA**
EWP Affiliated East-West Press
PVT, Ltd
G-I/16, Ansari Road, Darya Gany
New Delhi 110 002
Oxford Book and Stationery Co.
Scindia House, New Delhi 110 001;
17 Park Street, Calcutta 700 016
Oxford Subscription Agency
Institute for Development
Education
1 Anasuya Ave., Kilpauk
Madras 600 010
Periodical Expert Book Agency
D-42, Vivek Vihar, Delhi 110095

**• IRAN**
The FAO Bureau, International and
Regional Specialized
Organizations Affairs
Ministry of Agriculture of the Islamic
Republic of Iran
Keshavarz Bld, M.O.A., 17th floor
Teheran

**• IRELAND**
Publications Section
Government Stationery Office
4-5 Harcourt Road
Dublin 2

**• ISRAEL**
R.O.Y. International
P.O. Box 13056
Tel Aviv 61130

**• ITALY**
Libreria Scientifica Dott. Lucio de
Biasio "Aeiou"
Via Coronelli 6
20146 Milano
Libreria Concessionaria Sansoni
S.p.A. "Licosa"
Via Duca di Calabria 1/1
50125 Firenze

**FAO Bookshop**
Viale delle Terme di Caracalla
00100 Roma
Tel.  52255688
Fax  52255155
E-mail: publications-sales@fao.org
- **JAPAN**
**Far Eastern Booksellers**
**(Kyokuto Shoten Ltd)**
12 Kanda-Jimbocho 2 chome
Chiyoda-ku - P.O. Box 72
Tokyo 101-91
**Maruzen Company Ltd**
P.O. Box 5050
Tokyo International 100-31
- **KENYA**
**Text Book Centre Ltd**
Kijabe Street, P.O. Box 47540
Nairobi
- **LUXEMBOURG**
**M.J. De Lannoy**
202, avenue du Roi
1060 Bruxelles (Belgique)
- **MALAYSIA**
*Electronic products only:*
**Southbound**
Sendirian Berhad Publishers
9 College Square
01250 Penang
- **MALI**
**Librairie Traore**
Rue Soundiata Keita X 115
B.P. 3243
Bamako
- **MAROC**
**La Librairie Internationale**
70 Rue T'ssoule
B.P. 302 (RP)
Rabat
Tel. (07) 75-86-61
- **MEXICO**
**Librería, Universidad Autónoma**
**de Chapingo**
56230 Chapingo
**Libros y Editoriales S.A.**
Av. Progreso N° 202-1° Piso A
Apdo. Postal 18922, Col. Escandón
11800 México D.F.
- **NETHERLANDS**
**Roodveldt Import b.v.**
Brouwersgracht 288
1013 HG Amsterdam
- **NEW ZEALAND**
**Legislation Services**
P.O. Box 12418
Thorndon, Wellington
- **NICARAGUA**
**Librería HISPAMER**
Costado Este Univ. Centroamericana
Apdo. Postal A-221
Managua
- **NIGERIA**
**University Bookshop (Nigeria) Ltd**
University of Ibadan
Ibadan
- **NORWAY**
**Narvesen Info Center**
Bertrand Narvesens vei 2
P.O. Box 6125, Etterstad
0602 Oslo 6
Tel.  (+47) 22-57-33-00
Fax  (+47) 22-68-19-01
- **PAKISTAN**
**Mirza Book Agency**
65 Shahrah-e-Quaid-e-Azam
P.O. Box 729, Lahore 3
- **PARAGUAY**
**Librería INTERCONTINENTAL**
Editora e Impresora S.R.L.
Caballero 270 c/Mcal Estigarribia
Asunción

- **PERU**
**INDEAR**
Jirón Apurimac 375, Casilla 4937
Lima 1
- **PHILIPPINES**
**International Booksource Center (Phils)**
Room 1703, Cityland 10
Condominium Cor. Ayala Avenue &
H.V. de la Costa Extension
Makati, Metro Manila
- **POLAND**
**Ars Polona**
Krakowskie Przedmiescie 7
00-950 Warsaw
- **PORTUGAL**
**Livraria Portugal,**
**Dias e Andrade Ltda.**
Rua do Carmo 70-74, Apartado 2681
1117 Lisboa Codex
- **SINGAPORE**
**Select Books Pte Ltd**
03-15 Tanglin Shopping Centre
19 Tanglin Road
Singapore 1024
- **SOMALIA**
**"Samater's"**
P.O. Box 936
Mogadishu
- **SOUTH AFRICA**
**David Philip Publishers (Pty) Ltd**
P.O. Box 23408
Claremont 7735
South Africa
Tel.  Cape Town (021) 64-4136
Fax  Cape Town (021) 64-3358
- **SRI LANKA**
**M.D. Gunasena & Co. Ltd**
217 Olcott Mawatha, P.O. Box 246
Colombo 11
- **SUISSE**
**Buchhandlung und Antiquariat**
**Heinimann & Co.**
Kirchgasse 17
8001 Zurich
**UN Bookshop**
Palais des Nations
CH-1211 Genève 1
**Van Diermen Editions Techniques**
**ADECO**
Case Postale 465
CH-1211 Genève 19
- **SURINAME**
**Vaco n.v. in Suriname**
Domineestraat 26, P.O. Box 1841
Paramaribo
- **SWEDEN**
*Books and documents:*
**C.E. Fritzes**
P.O. Box 16356
103 27 Stockholm
*Subscriptions:*
**Vennergren-Williams AB**
P.O. Box 30004
104 25 Stockholm
- **THAILAND**
**Suksapan Panit**
Mansion 9, Rajdamnern Avenue
Bangkok
- **TOGO**
**Librairie du Bon Pasteur**
B.P. 1164
Lomé
- **TUNISIE**
**Société tunisienne de diffusion**
5, avenue de Carthage
Tunis
- **TURKEY**
**Kultur Yayiniari is - Turk Ltd Sti.**
Ataturk Bulvari N° 191, Kat. 21
Ankara
**Bookshops in Istanbul and Izmir**

- **UNITED KINGDOM**
**HMSO Publications Centre**
51 Nine Elms Lane
London SW8 5DR
Tel. (071) 873 9090 (orders)
     (071) 873 0011 (inquiries)
Fax (071) 873 8463
**and through HMSO Bookshops**
*Electronic products only:*
**Microinfo Ltd**
P.O. Box 3, Omega Road, Alton
Hampshire GU34 2PG
Tel. (0420) 86848
Fax (0420) 89889
- **URUGUAY**
**Librería Agropecuaria S.R.L.**
Buenos Aires 335
Casilla 1755
Montevideo C.P. 11000
- **USA**
*Publications:*
**UNIPUB**
4611/F Assembly Drive
Lanham MD 20706-4391
Toll-free 800 274-4888
Fax 301-459-0056
*Periodicals:*
**Ebsco Subscription Services**
P.O. Box 1431
Birmingham AL 35201-1431
Tel.  (205)991-6600
Telex 78-2661
Fax  (205)991-1449
**The Faxon Company Inc.**
15 Southwest Park
Westwood MA 02090
Tel. 6117-329-3350
Telex 95-1980
Cable FW Faxon Wood
- **VENEZUELA**
**Tecni-Ciencia Libros S.A.**
Torre Phelps-Mezzanina
Plaza Venezuela
Caracas
Tel. 782 8697/781 9945/781 9954
**Tamanaco Libros Técnicos S.R.L.**
Centro Comercial Ciudad Tamanaco
Nivel C-2
Caracas
Tel. 261 3344/261 3335/959 0016
**Tecni-Ciencia Libros, S.A.**
Centro Comercial, Shopping Center
Av. Andrés Eloy, Urb. El Prebo
Valencia, Ed. Carabobo
Tel. 222 724
**Fudeco, Librería**
Avenida Libertador-Este
Ed. Fudeco, Apartado 254
Barquisimeto C.P. 3002, Ed. Lara
Tel.  (051) 538 022
Fax  (051) 544 394
Télex (051) 513 14 FUDEC VC
**Fundación La Era Agrícola**
Calle 31 Junín Qta
Coromoto 5-49, Apartado 456
Mérida
**Librería FAGRO**
Universidad Central de Venezuela (UCV)
Maracay
- **ZIMBABWE**
**Grassroots Books**
100 Jason Moyo Avenue
P.O. Box A 267, Avondale
Harare;
61a Fort Street
Bulawayo

**Other countries / Autres pays / Otros países**
Distribution and Sales Section
Publications Division, FAO
Viale delle Terme di Caracalla
00100 Rome, Italy
Tel.  (39-6) 52251
Fax  (39-6) 52253152
Telex 625852/625853/610181 FAO I
E-mail: publications-sales@fao.org